STUDY IN DEVELOPMENT

Medicine and Public Health 1450 to the Present Day

STEPHEN LEE

General Editor: Josh Brooman

LONGMAN

Introduction · Unit 1 · Medicine and health before 1450

This book begins in the year 1450. This date is roughly the end of a long period in time known as the Middle Ages, which was sandwiched between the Ancient World and the Modern World. The three periods relate to one another in the following way:

Ancient or Classical World (especially Greece and Rome)
To about AD 450

Middle Ages or Medieval World
From about 450 to about 1450

Modern World
From about 1450

This Unit looks back from 1450 to find out (a) how the Ancient World influenced the Middle Ages and (b) how much the Middle Ages changed from the Ancient World. Unit 2 will make the connection between the Middle Ages and the Modern World. We should, however, be aware that these are very loose terms, used by historians for convenience. We should not expect any sudden change around 450 or 1450.

1.1 Influences of the Ancient World

The main period of Greek civilisation was the first thousand years BC. Greek civilisation was taken over by Rome, which reached the extent shown in Source 1. The Roman Empire eventually collapsed in AD 476. During this period of 1,500 years the Greeks and Romans made a great

Source 1

The Ancient World

Greek States about 400 B.C.
Roman Empire about 250 A.D.

deal of **progress** in medicine and health. That is to say, they changed many things for the better. But they also left gaps in that knowledge which had to be filled later.

How much progress was made by the Ancient World?

The Greeks made the main advances in medicine and theory, while both the Greeks and the Romans made important contributions to public health.

The work of Hippocrates

Hippocrates lived and worked in the fourth century BC on the island of Kos near Greece. He took a new approach to medicine, seeing it as a science and not as a branch of religion. Most people at this time believed that fate or the gods caused illness as a form of disapproval and that only their priests could cure them. Hippocrates, however, argued that natural causes should be sought for illness:

Source 2

A Greek carving of a patient being examined by a physician.

Source 3

Hippocrates on the reason for sickness.

Sickness is not sent by the gods or taken away by them. It has a physical basis. If we can find the cause we can cure the disease.

The cause could be found through careful observation. A prognosis, or assessment, could then be made of what was wrong, and treatment suggested (see Source 2). This approach, which is called *clinical observation*, is still used by doctors today. Hippocrates believed that the body should be encouraged to assist recovery through good food, exercise and fresh air. Drugs were prescribed only as the next step.

Hippocrates is remembered above all for the Hippocratic oath, which is a set of rules for the behaviour and conduct of physicians:

Source 4

An extract from the Hippocratic oath.

I will use treatment to help the sick according to my ability and judgement but never with a view to injury or wrongdoing. I will not give poison to anybody. ...Whatever I see or hear professionally or in my private life which ought not be to told I will keep secret.

The work of Galen

Galen was a Greek who was appointed chief physician to a school for gladiators in Rome. He gave far more attention than Hippocrates to anatomy (the structure of the human body). He found out about its working by dissecting corpses. He then published his findings. Among other things, he believed that blood passed through the lungs and he pointed out the importance of the spine:

Source 5

Galen, *On Anatomical Procedures*, about AD 175.

If you wish to paralyse all the parts of the body below this section and stop any movement...then sever the spinal marrow with a cut running completely through so that no parts remain joined together.

Galen claimed to be the greatest expert on anatomy and physiology, and his reputation lasted for the next 1,500 years.

Public health, cleanliness and exercise

The Greeks, in particular, played a wide range of sports as a compulsory part of their education. Both the Greeks and the Romans were very concerned to keep clean through regular washing and bathing. The Romans introduced huge public building programmes for this. They carefully chose healthy sites for their towns and villages. They also built aqueducts to carry water to the towns to avoid pollution and to provide the population with up to 1,350,000,000 litres of drinking water each day (see Sources 6 and 7). It was remarkable that they did this, since they had no knowledge about germs carried in water.

Source 6

The remains of the Claudian aqueduct near Rome. This was one of the main means of carrying fresh water into the city.

Source 7

Strabo's description of the water supply in Rome in the first century BC. Strabo was a Greek geographer.

Water is brought into the city through aqueducts in such quantities that it is like a river flowing through the city. Almost every house has cisterns and water pipes and fountains.

The Romans also provided public baths in every town they built, and a complex system of latrines which were flushed by water.

The gaps left by the Ancient World

The Greeks and the Romans had some shortcomings in their approach to medicine. For example, they made little headway in understanding the causes of disease. Hippocrates insisted that illness occurred when one of the body's four humours (liquids) was out of balance with the others. These were blood, phlegm and black and yellow bile. There was no understanding yet that the humours might be the symptoms of disease which was actually being caused by something else. Hence doctors recommended natural remedies, or herbs, or certain types of foods. These generally did little harm and might even have done some good. But doctors also used bleeding to rebalance the blood humour. This meant taking a certain amount of blood from a vein. It was a practice which lasted for the next 1,500 years and which was nearly always harmful, causing infection or anaemia (shortage of red blood cells).

There were also limits to the understanding of anatomy, despite the work done on this by Galen.

Questions

1 What did the ancient Greeks contribute to the development of medical knowledge and health care?

2 How did the Romans tackle the problem of public health?

3 'The contribution of the ancients to medicine and health was impressive but incomplete.' Explain why you agree or disagree.

1.2 The Middle Ages

As we have seen, the Romans and Greeks made progress in many ways. Then, in the fifth century, Germanic tribes invaded the Roman Empire and overthrew the last Roman emperor in AD 476. During the Middle Ages, which followed the collapse of Rome, there were further changes. In some ways, medical knowledge and health went backwards, or experienced **regress** (the opposite to progress). In other ways, the Middle Ages continued to use the ideas and influences of the Ancient World. This is known as **continuity**.

Were the Middle Ages a time of regress or of continuity?

Regress
Various factors brought regress to medicine and health in the Middle Ages.

The Church's control of ideas
The Church was a negative influence on medicine for several reasons. In the first place, it controlled the spread of ideas:

Source 1

Vernon Coleman, *The Story of Medicine*, 1985.

The close relationship between medicine and religion which had been thrown aside by Hippocrates was now back with a vengeance....The Christian religion, which dominated medical thinking, halted progress in Europe for the best part of a millennium.

The Church opposed the study of the human body in any detail. It believed that dissection would prevent the resurrection of the complete body after a person's death. There was therefore a complete lack of further scientific research and Galen's ideas were accepted as unchangeable. As for disease, this was seen as a sign of God's punishment for human sins. Cures were therefore sought in prayer, or punishment, or by appealing to the saints.

The increase in filth and squalor

In Roman times most of the population had been protected against disease not so much by medicine as by measures for public health. During the Middle Ages the standard of public health dropped.

There were two main sources of filth. One was the human excrement which was found in huge quantities throughout the cities and in all the rivers. The King of England was so disgusted that he complained:

Source 2

King Edward III in a letter to the Lord Mayor of London, 1349.

...the streets and lanes through which people had to pass were foul with human faeces and the air of the city poisoned to the great danger of men passing, especially in this time of infectious disease.

faeces Excrement.

Almost as bad were rubbish and animal remains. Animals were slaughtered in alleys and back streets and the remains left to fester.

These conditions had serious effects. First, the rubbish harboured vast numbers of rats which, of course, carried diseases. Second, the general state of filth and lack of personal hygiene greatly reduced the resistance of the people to infection. This meant that diseases were more likely to appear in towns in the Middle Ages than in ancient times, and that people were less likely to be able to resist them.

The growth of epidemics

The worst epidemic ever to affect Europe occurred between 1347 and 1350 (see Sources 3 and 4). Known as the Black Death, it killed between a quarter and a half of the whole population of Europe. In Britain the population fell from 4 million to 2 million.

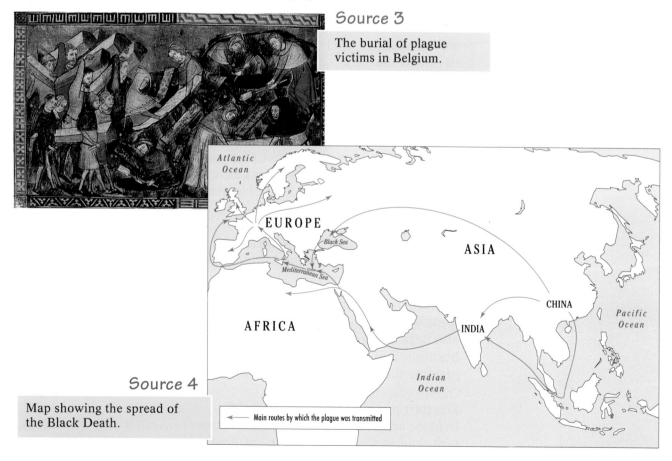

Source 3

The burial of plague victims in Belgium.

Source 4

Map showing the spread of the Black Death.

← Main routes by which the plague was transmitted

The symptoms were described by an Italian writer, Boccaccio:

Source 5

Giovanni Boccaccio, *The Decameron*, written between 1348 and 1353.

tumour A swelling.

> In men and women alike it first betrayed itself by the emergence of certain tumours in the groin or the armpits, some of which grew as large as a common apple, others as an egg.

One form of the disease, pneumonic plague, was passed on from person to person. The more common form, bubonic plague, was the result of the bite of a flea from a black rat (whose scientific name is *Rattus rattus*). The effect of the Black Death was a shock: no one had the least idea as to what caused it or how to deal with it. Some considered that it was a natural catastrophe:

Source 6

A description by an Italian chronicler (based on hearsay).

Cathay China.

> Between Cathay and Persia there rained a vast rain of fire; falling in flakes like snow and burning up mountains and plains and other lands, with men and women; and then arose vast masses of smoke; and whomsoever beheld this died within the space of half a day; and likewise any man or woman who looked upon those who had seen this.

To ward off this horror, people might be bled to release the 'foul humours' or, alternatively, they could sniff posies of flowers. Other remedies are summarised by a modern historian:

Source 7

Philip Ziegler, *The Black Death*, 1969.

potent Powerful.

> A fig or two with some rue and filberts taken before breakfast was a useful start to the day. Pills of aloes, myrrh and saffron were popular. One authority placed his confidence in ten-year-old treacle blended with some sixty elements, including chopped-up snakes, and mixed with good wine. ...[Another] recommended powdered emerald; a remedy so potent that, if a toad looked at it, its eyes would crack.

Some saw the Black Death as a punishment for sins. They therefore thought that flagellation (self-whipping) would help. Others thought that Jews were responsible and that they should be removed from society. This meant an increase in their persecution. No one seemed to think of the black rat or the flea as a direct cause of the plague. No one considered that the filthy streets and lack of hygiene might also be responsible.

Continuity
In some ways, many of the ideas and practices of the Ancient World continued to be used in the Middle Ages.

The part played by monasteries
Many of the Roman manuscripts on medicine were stored in monasteries; some were copies by monks for use by people in the future. Monasteries also became the centres of care for the sick. They contained most of the hospitals and infirmaries in Europe and the monks frequently put into practice the ideas of Hippocrates.

The part played by the Arab world
In some areas ideas were also taken from the Arab world. The Arabs, in turn, had in their great library at Baghdad many of the ancient Greek

texts, so that these were as carefully preserved as the Roman ones. In fact, part of the Arab knowledge was based on Greek medicine. This came back to Europe as a result of Europe's contacts with the Arabs. These occurred during the Crusades and as a result of regular trading contacts with the Arabs, especially in the Italian port of Salerno. Here important medical schools were set up.

In addition to preserving Greek works, the Arabs added many of their own through doctors like Rhazes (860–925), Albicasis (936–1013) and Avicenna (980–1037). In many ways, the Arabs were therefore more advanced than Europeans.

Source 8

The Arab world in the Middle Ages and the points of contact with Europe.

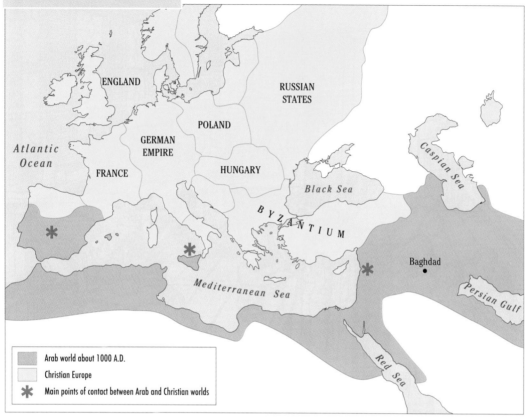

Arab world about 1000 A.D.

Christian Europe

* Main points of contact between Arab and Christian worlds

The need for further change

The Middle Ages were not, therefore, a period of medical progress. Indeed, it seemed that some of the ideas of the Ancient World were no longer being used. For any real progress to take place, it would be necessary to rediscover some of the skills of the Greeks and Romans – and then build something new on these.

This is precisely what happened during the period known as the Renaissance, to which we turn next.

Questions

1. What is meant by 'regress'? Explain how changes in public health between the Ancient World and the Middle Ages show 'regress'.

2. What is meant by 'continuity'? Give an example of continuity in medicine between the Ancient World and the Middle Ages.

3. Sources 5 and 6 were produced at the time. Source 7 is modern. Compare the value of these sources for an enquiry into the causes of the Black Death.

4. Give examples of religion
   a holding back
   b helping medical progress in the Middle Ages.

The title page of
Opus Chirurgicum by
Theophrastus Paracelsus,
1565.

This illustration is the title page of a book, published in 1565, by a Swiss scientist and doctor named Paracelsus. It shows the inside of a hospital at the time of the Renaissance. It consists of three separate sections, and there are five groups of figures. In the foreground are three learned men in discussion. The middle ground shows two men receiving different types of treatment, while the background reveals two patients being nursed in bed.

Does the picture represent a scene which actually occurred? Perhaps, but it is unlikely. Since it is a title page, its real purpose is probably *symbolic*; that is to say, it illustrates the different functions of medicine which are covered in Paracelsus's book. It also provides a good preview to what we are about to cover in Part 1. Units 2 and 3 look at the growth of new ideas as a result of the Renaissance and the Scientific Revolution. Unit 4 covers surgery, training and hospitals. The role of women is surveyed in Unit 5, and the strange behaviour of different diseases follows in Unit 6. The focus of Unit 7 is on the many people who practised medicine without any type of qualification. How many of these issues are symbolised by the illustration?

Unit 2 · The Renaissance and medicine

'Renaissance' means 'rebirth'. The Renaissance was a period, roughly between 1450 and 1600, in which many forms of culture, especially drawing, painting, sculpture and literature, took huge steps forward. People at the time were inspired partly by looking back to Ancient Greece and Rome, and partly by trying out ideas which were new. The earliest centre of the Renaissance was Italy. It then spread to other parts of Europe, including Germany, the Netherlands, France and England.

Another feature of the Renaissance was the growth of interest in other parts of the world. This was stimulated by voyages of discovery to areas in America and Asia which had previously been unknown.

Changes during the Renaissance

Source 1

Michelangelo: sketch for
The Resurrection

Things happen when a catalyst speeds up the process of change. A catalyst is therefore an agent of change. Water, for example, boils as a result of the catalyst of heat. We can also use the word in an historical sense. In some ways, the new ideas of the Renaissance in art, literature and travel speeded up changes taking place at the same time in medicine.

How did the Renaissance act as a catalyst?

The effects of painting and drawing

Artists of the Renaissance helped the cause of medical knowledge a great deal. Michelangelo's sculptures and paintings of the human figure were highly accurate because he had a detailed interest in anatomy (see Source 1). The same applied to the work of Leonardo da Vinci.

The effects of printing

One of the great changes brought by the Renaissance was the printing press. This was partly the result of a huge increase in the demand for information:

Source 2

Vernon Coleman, *The Story of Medicine,* 1985.

By the fifteenth century students and scholars all around Europe were hungry for books and for the information they contained. One bookseller in Florence was said to have employed up to fifty scribes, and in monasteries throughout Europe monks were busy copying out volumes of all kinds. Printing techniques were not improved by accident; they were an inevitable result of a steadily increasing demand for knowledge and reading matter of all kinds.

In turn, the availability of printing presses meant that medical ideas could be spread across all parts of Europe. They were no longer to be found only in manuscripts kept in the libraries of monasteries.

The effects of the voyages of discovery

Opening up South America brought many medical benefits. The best example was the import of quinine, an extract from cinchona bark. This was especially important for two reasons. One was specific: quinine provided an effective treatment for malaria. The other was more general: it formed the base of new forms of medicine and the beginning of a more modern approach to providing drugs. Quinine was connected with a specific disease because it had a proven success in curing it. The symptoms of other diseases were analysed more carefully to see if other cures might be more readily available. This was a first major step forwards from earlier cures based on folklore and superstition.

On the other hand, the voyages brought problems. The sailors of the expeditions of Columbus brought back syphilis to Europe (see page 32). Some products also contributed to disease. The import of sugar from the New World greatly increased the amount of tooth decay in Europe.

On balance, however, the effects of travel were favourable to medicine – not least because they opened up the eyes of medical writers to cures from other parts of the world.

Source 3

The title page of Vesalius's book *De Humani Corporis Fabrica*.

Who contributed most to the development of new ideas in medicine?

Most of the earlier medical ideas of the Renaissance period came from Europe. Gradually, however, people in England and Scotland also made their contributions.

Medical ideas on the Continent

A key figure was Andreas Vesalius (1514–64), who came from Brussels. He wrote the first major book on anatomy (*De Humani Corporis Fabrica* or *The Fabric of the Human Body*). This contained 277 anatomical illustrations. These were among the most famous ever produced. Two are provided here (Sources 3 and 4). One is the title page, which shows Vesalius conducting an anatomy lecture over a corpse to dozens of students.

Clearly, these illustrations benefited from the influence of the drawings of the great Renaissance painters.

Source 4

A skeleton from Vesalius's work. This shows an eye for detailed anatomy but is also posed, showing the influence of Renaissance artists.

It is difficult to exaggerate the importance of this work. According to a modern historian:

Source 5   W. Durant, *The Story of Civilisation*, 1967.

It was a revolution because it ended the reign of Galen in anatomy, revised the whole science in terms of dissection, and so established the physical basis of modern medicine, which begins with his book.

Another influential man of the Renaissance period was the Swiss scientist Paracelsus (1493–1541). His main contribution was to research widely throughout Europe and the Middle East for medical knowledge.

Source 6

A sixteenth-century painting of Paracelsus.

Source 7

Paracelsus on travel.

The doctor must be a traveller, because he must enquire of the world.

He challenged existing ideas about disease and tried out many different methods of curing illness. He added the important idea that the physician should look for specific symptoms for a disease and then prescribe a specific cure. Some of his methods lasted long after his death. For example, he prescribed mercury for the treatment of syphilis. He also preferred to allow wounds to drain rather than to pack them with dried dung, which had been a popular practice at the time.

Medical ideas in England

English physicians were strongly influenced by what was happening on the Continent, especially in Italy. Thomas Linacre (1461–1524) came from Canterbury, took a degree at Oxford and travelled to Italy. He translated some of the medical classics so that they could be understood more easily. He also set up the Royal College of Physicians, which established the qualifications for physicians.

John Caius (1510–73) came from Norwich and taught at Cambridge University; he too studied in Italy and was in close contact with Vesalius. He was also court physician to Henry VIII, Edward VI, Mary and Elizabeth. He refounded a Cambridge college as Gonville and Caius College and was President of the College of Physicians. He also provided a detailed description of the so-called 'sweating sickness'. Thomas Phaer (1510–60) wrote *The Book of Children*, the first work on paediatrics, or child medicine. It contained little that was original but took ideas from many parts of Europe and showed a willingness to try a variety of remedies.

The persistence of older ideas

For the arts, the Renaissance was a period of 'peak' achievement which it would be difficult to equal in the future. For medicine, however, it was only the beginning of a long series of changes. During the sixteenth century there were even some brakes on change, applied by older ideas which refused to die.

One of these was astrology, the study of the signs of the zodiac. This had been very widespread during the Middle Ages. Even during the Renaissance many physicians believed that the signs of the zodiac controlled the functions and health of different parts of the body. Diagnosis would therefore be based on the signs of the zodiac rather than on the methods of Paracelsus.

What was now needed was a new wave of change which would do for science what the Renaissance had done for the arts. If medicine had benefited from painting, how much more would it do so from changes in physics, biology and mathematics? Such a change occurred in the seventeenth century, in the form of the Scientific Revolution.

Questions	
1	The Renaissance was mainly concerned with the arts and the discovery of other lands. How did this benefit medicine?
2	In what different ways do Sources 2, 3, 4, 5 and 7 show the importance of communication in medicine?
3	Who, in your opinion, was more important in the history of medicine: Vesalius or Paracelsus? Explain your choice.
4	What effect do you think illustrations like Sources 3 and 4 would have had in the sixteenth century on **a** patients **b** doctors **c** the general public?
5	Write a brief account of two viewpoints from doctors in the sixteenth century – one in support of Vesalius, the other opposing his ideas.

Unit 3 · Medical developments in the seventeenth century

In Unit 2 we examined the Renaissance of the fifteenth and sixteenth centuries, which had affected medicine as well as the arts. We also considered the way in which various factors combined to make this possible. We now turn to the seventeenth century which, in some ways, was a period of even more rapid progress. We shall again see a range of influences, but this time we shall add another ingredient by looking at the work of **innovators** (those who introduce new ideas) and **consolidators** (those who put these new ideas into practice).

3.1 Medical progress in the seventeenth century

Medical research today is carried out mainly in research institutes or in university laboratories. The people who do this are usually trained experts or specialists: this will be their main job. The same did not apply in the seventeenth century. Far less was then known about the sciences and there were no experts as such. Nevertheless, rapid progress did take place. Why?

What conditions favoured medical progress?

A 'Scientific Revolution'

During the seventeenth century changes took place in all branches of the sciences, especially in mathematics, physics and astronomy. These were introduced by people who had a wide variety of interests. They were not experts or specialists. Rather, they were 'gifted amateurs', who 'dabbled' in what interested them and often achieved a 'breakthrough' in the process. One of the most important was the Frenchman, René Descartes (1596–1650), who developed a new method of reasoning. He was determined

Source 1

René Descartes, *Discourse on Method*, 1641.

never to accept anything for true which I clearly did not know to be such.

He aimed to build up his knowledge 'by beginning with objects the simplest' and then 'to ascend little by little to the knowledge of the more complex'. This process is known as 'deductive reasoning'. Also of considerable importance were Galileo, who developed the telescope, and Isaac Newton, who deduced the law of gravitation. In fact, there were so many changes that the whole process is sometimes called the Scientific Revolution.

The impact of the Scientific Revolution on medicine

Medical changes in the seventeenth century were greatly influenced by four developments in the Scientific Revolution.

1 The method of deductive reasoning, developed by Descartes, fitted perfectly the needs of medicine. The physician learned how to make deductions from his patient's symptoms to diagnose what was wrong – in effect, rediscovering the method of Hippocrates. Medical research also benefited. As one writer produced an idea, others developed it in different ways, gradually increasing the range of medical knowledge.

2 Seventeenth-century scientists had a new attitude to the human body. Descartes saw it as a piece of complex machinery. In doing this he removed some of the prejudices against examining it in every detail.

3 Many scientific developments had a spin-off which benefited medicine. For example, Galileo's work on telescopes meant increased knowledge about lenses. This, in turn, encouraged men like Anton van Leeuwenhoek to use them in an entirely new way – as a microscope. Thus the observation of the largest bodies – the stars and planets – led directly to knowledge about the smallest – blood cells and bacteria.

4 Countries competed with each other in setting up learned societies. Italy had the Accademia dei Lincei and France the Académie des Sciences. England's equivalent was the Royal Society. This was set up in 1645 as a discussion group for scientists who aimed at the 'improvement of natural knowledge'. King Charles II granted a Royal Charter in 1663. This greatly encouraged the spread of interest in new medical ideas and works. It also led to the publication of journals. This was important because it meant that one discovery could be followed up by others connected to it. There was therefore a *chain* of development.

Question	Did medicine benefit more from the non-medical changes of the Scientific Revolution than from those of the Renaissance? Explain your view by referring to Units 2 and 3.1.

3.2 Innovators and consolidators

Change usually takes place as a result of the work of two types of person. The **innovator** develops new ideas or makes a major discovery as a result of careful research. The **consolidator**, on the other hand, makes a contribution by patiently adding smaller changes. The innovator and consolidator depend on each other. Without the innovator, no new ideas would come about. Without the consolidator, changes would not reach out very far. Together they contribute to a broad pattern of change.

In seventeenth-century England there was one major innovator – William Harvey. There were several important consolidators – Robert Boyle, Robert Hooke, John Mayow and, above all, Thomas Sydenham.

William Harvey

His career

William Harvey (1578–1657) was born in Folkestone. He studied at King's School, Canterbury, and Caius College, Cambridge, where he received an MD (Doctor of Medicine). He travelled widely through France, Germany and Italy, before serving at St Bartholomew's Hospital and as physician to both James I and Charles I.

His work

William Harvey is best known for his research into the movement of blood in the body. Many scientists still believed in Galen's theory that blood was made by the liver and that it moved through the veins to the limbs and organs. There it was used up and more had to be made.

Harvey came to a very different conclusion. He argued that the blood was circulated round the body by the heart, not the liver. The heart was a pump, which drove the blood through arteries and veins to various parts of the body. The blood did not move backwards and forwards through the veins, but circulated to the veins via the arteries. Above all, the amount of blood in the body did not change. Nor was it used up; instead, it recirculated:

Source 1

William Harvey, *On the Motion of the Heart and Blood,* 1628.

…it will be manifest that the blood circulates, revolves, propelled and then returning, from the heart to the extremities to the heart, and thus that it performs a kind of circular motion…and is in a state of ceaseless motion; that this is the act or function which the heart performs by means of its pulse; and that it is the sole and only means of the motion and contraction of the heart.

This was based upon the most careful observation. Harvey dissected animals and the corpses of executed criminals. He also experimented with ligatures to show that by stopping the normal flow of blood and placing the finger at certain points it can be proved that blood travels one way through the arteries. This is shown in Source 2.

Harvey attracted a great deal of support – and opposition – during his lifetime and there was much debate about the circulation of blood. He was, however, fortunate to receive the protection of King Charles I, to whom he is shown explaining his theory in Source 3.

Source 2

An illustration from Harvey's book.

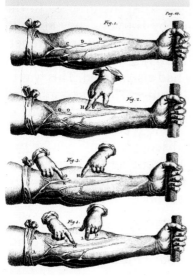

Source 3

William Harvey and King Charles I, painted by Robert Hannah (1812–1909).

Views on Harvey's work

Historians seem to agree about the importance of Harvey and his work. Sources 4–7 are some examples:

Source 4

Garrison, *An Introduction to the History of Medicine*, 1929.

The discovery of the circulation itself was the most momentous event in medical history since Galen's time.

Source 5

Roderick McGrew, *Encyclopaedia of Medical History*, 1985.

Nothing comparable to Harvey's theory developed for 200 years.

Source 6

Talbot, *A Biographical History of Medicine*, 1970.

The conclusion of most historians...is that Harvey was one of the greatest physiologists of all time.

physiologist Expert on the organs of the body.

Source 7

Notable Medical Books (no author), 1976.

Harvey's small book is usually considered the most important single medical work ever published.

How important was Harvey's work?

Are the views in Sources 4 to 7 fully justified? We can argue this in two ways.

On the one hand, they are. Harvey inspired many other investigations and works about the circulation of blood and the function of the heart. A huge number of 'consolidators' followed, both on the Continent and in England. For example, Marcello Malpighi (1628–94) and Anton van Leeuwenhoek (1632–1723) both used microscopes to detect the capillaries which enabled the blood to pass from the arteries to the veins. This process had not been explained by Harvey. They also did work on blood cells which, again, Harvey had not discovered. Robert Boyle (1627–91) and Robert Hooke (1635–1703) provided a reason for the circulation of the blood, which Harvey had also missed. This was to supply the parts of the body with air from the lungs. This was confirmed by John Mayow (1643–79), who believed that some life-giving part of the air entered the blood when a person drew breath. This part was eventually detected a century later by the discovery of oxygen by two scientists, Joseph Priestley and Antoine Laurent de Lavoisier. Thus Harvey started a chain reaction, with each question raising a new answer and each answer raising a new question.

On the other hand, it took a long time for Harvey's work to show any practical benefits. Blood transfusions were attempted, but were not effective since nothing was yet known about blood grouping. Also, common practices from the past, such as blood-letting, were still widely used fifty years after Harvey's death. Surgery was hardly affected at all (see Unit 4.1) because any sort of operation on the heart was out of the question until the twentieth century. Even physicians did not really learn how to use the pressure points of the arteries in their diagnosis. Not until the twentieth century was the pulse of any patient taken as a matter of course.

Thomas Sydenham

His career

Thomas Sydenham (see Source 8) studied at Oxford and Montpellier, in France. His career was interrupted by the English Civil War between King and Parliament and he spent time as a captain of horse in Cromwell's army. Later, he became a well-known general practitioner in London, and was described as 'a trooper turned physician'.

Source 8

A seventeenth-century portrait of Thomas Sydenham (1624–89)

His work

Sydenham cannot be seen as an innovator in the mould of Harvey. He was not a researcher and he made no great original discovery. He was very much a consolidator. He was a careful observer and recorded his observations in great detail. He stressed practical common sense rather than theory. For this reason he is often known as the 'English Hippocrates'.

His main work was *Medical Observations*, published in 1676. This was a careful record and description of diseases in London between 1661 and 1675. These descriptions included cholera, dysentery, measles and scarlatina. He also wrote a famous paper on gout and another on hysteria. He developed a theory of disease based on observation. He considered that there were two main types of symptom. 'Essential symptoms' came from outside the body, 'accidental symptoms' from inside – in the form of the body's resistance. Hence a fever was an 'accidental symptom', showing the attempt of the body to throw off an 'external symptom'.

All of Sydenham's ideas and theories came from constant experience and observation. Sources 9 and 10 show this quite clearly.

Source 9

Thomas Sydenham on the learning of medicine.

The art of medicine is to be properly learned only from its practice and its exercise.

Source 10

Thomas Sydenham on observation.

You must go to the bedside; it is there alone you can learn disease.

Sydenham practised what he preached. His own observations were meticulous and detailed, as in Sources 11 and 12.

Source 11

Sydenham describes the symptoms of chorea, a nervous disorder.

'Chorea Sancti Viti' is a sort of Convulsion, which chiefly invades Boys and Girls, from the age of ten Years of Age to Puberty: First, it shows itself by a certain Lameness, or rather Instability of one of the Legs, which the Patient drags after him like a Fool; afterward it appears in the Hand of the same side; which he that is affected with this Disease, can by no means keep in the same Posture for one moment.

Source 12

Sydenham describes the symptoms of gouty arthritis.

He goes to Bed and sleeps well, but about Two a Clock in the Morning, is waked by the Pain, seizing either his great Toe, the Heel, the Calf of the Leg, or the Ankle; this Pain is like that of dislocated Bones, with the Sense as it were of Water almost cold, poured upon the Membranes of the Parts affected, presently shivering and shaking follow with a feverish Disposition.

How important was Sydenham's work?

As with Harvey, there are two sides to Sydenham's achievements. Some of his ideas were old-fashioned. He believed, for example, that diseases were caused by foul airs or 'miasmas' and he continued to recommend bleeding as a form of treatment. The other side is that Sydenham had a great deal of influence on practical medicine. One of his many followers was Walter Harris (1647–1732), who applied Sydenham's techniques of observation to produce a paper on the diseases of infants. A modern historian places Sydenham almost on a par with Harvey:

Source 13

Vernon Coleman, *The Story of Medicine*, 1985.

Thomas Sydenham established a new tradition of clinical observation ...which was, in its own way, as revolutionary as the 'discoveries' of the experimentalists.

Questions

1 This Unit describes Harvey as an 'innovator' and Sydenham as a 'consolidator'. Find as many reasons as you can to support this view.

2 Can you see any ways in which Harvey might be seen as a 'consolidator' and Sydenham as an 'innovator'?

3 How useful are the illustrations provided in Sources 2 and 3 for the study of Harvey's work?

4 Harvey's work had little practical effect on the practice of medicine in the short term. Does this mean that the opinions given in Sources 4, 5, 6 and 7 are wrong?

5 Why has Sydenham been called the English Hippocrates? Study Sources 11, 12 and 13, and give examples of how his methods were similar to those of Hippocrates.

6 Which of Harvey or Sydenham made the more important contribution to medicine in the seventeenth century? Explain your answer, using the sources and your own knowledge.

Unit 4 · Surgery, medical training and hospital care

4.1 Surgical achievements in the sixteenth and seventeenth centuries

Most of the earliest achievements in surgery took place on the Continent. Gradually, however, the lead was taken by Britain, especially the cities of Edinburgh and London.

Source 1

Portrait of Ambroise Paré (1510–90).

Surgery on the Continent

The finest surgeon of the Renaissance period was Ambroise Paré (see Source 1). He gained enormous experience in surgery through service in the French army, which was involved in numerous wars during the sixteenth century. He relied very much on first-hand observation and frequently criticised those who based their ideas about surgery on theory alone:

Source 2

Paré replying to one of his critics.

Dare you teach me Surgery, you who have never come out of your study? Surgery is learned by the eye and by the hands.

There is one particularly well-known incident involving Paré. One night he found that he had run out of the hot oil which was used to cauterise (seal) wounds. He therefore improvised with what he had available, using a mixture of turpentine, rose oil and egg yolk.

Source 3

Paré describing his discovery of a new treatment for wounds.

That night I slept badly. I was afraid that the ones I had not cauterised would be poisoned. I got up at daybreak and visited them. Much to my surprise, those to whom I had applied my lotion had had a good night, they had little pain and their wounds were not inflamed or swollen. Those who had been treated with boiling oil were feverish and in pain; their wounds were swollen....When I had many times tried this... I thought...that neither I nor any other should ever cauterise any wounded with gunshot.

From there, Paré went on to suggest that boiling oil should no longer be used on wounds. But how should the flow of blood be stopped after an amputation? Instead of a cautery, Paré said, surgeons should use a ligature, or a belt tightened round the arteries. This saved many lives and reduced the pain.

Source 4

A nineteenth-century picture of Paré applying a ligature on the battlefield.

Source 5

Paré describing the result of one of his amputations.

I returned to Paris with the gentleman whose leg I had cut off. He said he had got off cheap, not to have been miserably burned to stop the blood.

Paré therefore added a great deal of common sense to surgery. Another great surgeon, who lived in the eighteenth century, was Giovanni Morgnani (1682–1771). His contribution was rather more scientific. He taught students how to dissect bodies which had been infected by disease or deformed by wounds. He showed that post-mortem studies could be used to train surgeons how to locate the place to make an incision.

Surgery in Britain

Between 1450 and 1750 a number of surgeons made names for themselves in England and Scotland. Although not as famous as Paré, they were nevertheless important as consolidators (see Unit 3). They were often teachers of anatomy as well.

Thomas Vicary (1494–1561) was court surgeon to Henry VII and did a great deal to reorganise the profession (see below). William Clowes (1540–1604) was a man very much after Paré's own heart. In addition to being surgeon to Elizabeth I and at St Bartholomew's Hospital, he also served with the English army in Flanders and with the English navy against the Spanish Armada. He is particularly well known for a book on gunshot wounds, as is Thomas Gale (1507–86). John Woodall (1569–1643) had experience abroad with the English East India Company. His most popular book was *The Surgeon's Mate*, a detailed description of the surgical instruments a ship should have before setting out to sea.

During the eighteenth century three names are especially associated with developments in surgery. William Cheselden (1688-1752), who practised at St Thomas's Hospital, introduced a 90-second operation for the removal of a gall-bladder stone. He also wrote a paper on bones. William Hunter and his brother, John Hunter, are remembered for their contributions to the art of dissection and for their collection of specimens. As we shall see shortly, they also played a major part in training others.

Source 6

'The Amputation', from a German book published in 1716.

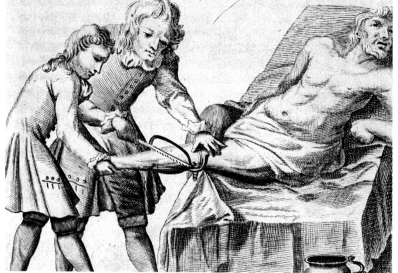

What obstacles remained to further progress in surgery?

Any breakthrough in surgery was prevented by two major problems. One was the filth which existed in hospitals and operating theatres. Few surgeons yet associated infection with germs and there was no thought of sterilising operating instruments. The other problem was the absence of any anaesthetic, which meant that the patient would have to be operated on while fully conscious (see Source 6). Surgery therefore had to be quick, which prevented it from being complex. These issues are dealt with in further detail in Unit 10.

Questions

1 To what extent is the advice in Source 2 put into practice in Source 3?

2 Explain how the methods of Paré and Morgnani differed from each other. How might they have been used to help each other?

3 'The contribution of Britain to surgery between 1450 and 1750 was not very important.' Do you agree with this? Give reasons.

4 Examine Sources 4 and 6. Source 6 was produced at the time, Source 4 about 300 years after the event. Is Source 6 more valuable than Source 4 for a study of surgical methods?

4.2 Medical organisation and training

The medical profession has always had different branches. In the sixteenth and seventeenth centuries there were three: the physicians, the apothecaries and the surgeons. Physicians regarded themselves as superior to the others. Apothecaries produced drugs and potions. Surgeons were often barbers as well, and this type was called the barber-surgeon. Outside his barber shop he placed a pole with red and white stripes, which represented blood and bandages. Barber-surgeons were not popular with others in the profession. William Clowes, himself a surgeon, said that they were...

Source 1

A painting by Hogarth showing an eighteenth-century barber-surgeon's shop.

Source 2 William Clowes, a sixteenth-century English surgeon.

...no better than runagates or vagabonds ...shameless in countenance, lewd in disposition, brutish in judgement and understanding.

There were various attempts to make sure that physicians and surgeons were properly qualified. Thomas Linacre, for example, secured the foundation of the Royal College of Physicians in 1551. This was intended to license physicians throughout the country. Meanwhile, Thomas Vicary had persuaded Henry VIII to establish the United Company of Barber-Surgeons. The idea here was to confine the barber's activities to cutting hair – and pulling out teeth.

The results were not very satisfactory. Physicians and surgeons despised each other, and the barber-surgeons were as active as ever. What really made a difference in the long term was not laws passed by monarchs, but the growth of surgery in the universities. The example came from the first medical teaching university in Europe. This was at Leyden, in the Dutch Republic, and was run by a world-famous medical lecturer. Herman Boerhaave encouraged the study of various branches of the sciences, including physics, chemistry, anatomy and physiology. He has been called 'the father of modern medical education', and some of his pupils went on to practise the same ideas at Edinburgh University, which was set up in 1681. By the late eighteenth century, when the Royal College of Surgeons was founded, Edinburgh had taken over as the leading university in Europe for surgical training.

In England, the main changes were made by the Hunter brothers. William Hunter founded a medical school in London. John Hunter, who had spent part of his life as an army surgeon, set up his consulting room and lecture rooms in Great Windmill Street, near Leicester Square. He put together a huge collection of specimens. He wrote a number of important works based on his observation. Lecturers were encouraged to buy a share of the school, and they paid themselves from the fees they charged their pupils.

Oxford University also set up an anatomy school and a small medical school, connected with the Radcliffe Infirmary. By the end of the period it was probably the third most important training centre in Britain, after Edinburgh and London.

What obstacles remained to progress in training?

Although the quality of medical training gradually improved, it was still very patchy:

Source 3

F. W. Cartwright, *A Social History of Medicine*, 1977.

> By the end of the eighteenth century it became apparent that English medical education varied considerably in standard and that the average was disturbingly low. Oxford and Cambridge awarded both degrees and licences but training approached the farcical. Sir Isaac Pennington …held the post of Linacre Lecturer of Medicine for fifty years…and the professorship of medicine for twenty-three years. During the whole of this [period]…he gave not a single lecture in any subject.

A survey showed that only 68 out of 266 medical practitioners in the North of England had had any training. Lincoln had a total of five physicians. To make matters worse, there was more and more need for qualified physicians and surgeons, as England was experiencing a major growth in population.

Questions

1. Explain why there was rivalry between physicians and surgeons.

2. How can Sources 1 and 2 be used as evidence that Thomas Vicary had not really succeeded in controlling the activities of the barber-surgeons?

3. Were the advances made in training during this period outweighed by the shortcomings?

4.3 Hospital care

During the Middle Ages, most of the infirmaries and hospitals had been in monasteries or convents. Even hospitals outside these were usually connected in some way with the Church, and had other functions such as caring for the poor. The earliest of the hospitals was probably at York in the tenth century. Another was St Bartholomew's Hospital in London in the twelfth century. By the later Middle Ages, however, the number of hospitals had begun to decline. This was due partly to the reduction of the population as a result of the Black Death.

During the sixteenth century much of the contribution made by the Church was lost when Henry VIII dissolved the monasteries. For several years there was no replacement. Eventually, Henry VIII agreed that some hospitals should be refounded as secular (non-religious) places of care:

Source 1

Henry VIII's permission to refound a hospital at Smithfield in 1544.

The abuses, in long lapses of time lamentably occurring, being reformed, we have endeavoured that henceforth there be comfort to the prisoners, shelter to the poor, visitation to the sick, food to the hungry, drink to the thirsty, clothes to the naked, and sepulchre to the dead.

The next development occurred in the eighteenth century, when many voluntary hospitals were founded. The benefactors were rich men with a desire to do good works, and the hospitals were staffed by unpaid volunteers. By 1750 the most famous hospitals in Britain were to be found in London. St Bartholomew's, shown in Source 2, was the oldest. Another was Westminster Hospital. A third was Guy's, founded and endowed by Thomas Guy, opening with 435 beds in 1725. St George's followed in 1734, the London Infirmary in 1740 and the Middlesex in 1746. All of these eventually became teaching hospitals and attract large numbers of students today.

Source 2

St Bartholomew's Hospital in 1710 (from an engraving by James Gibbs).

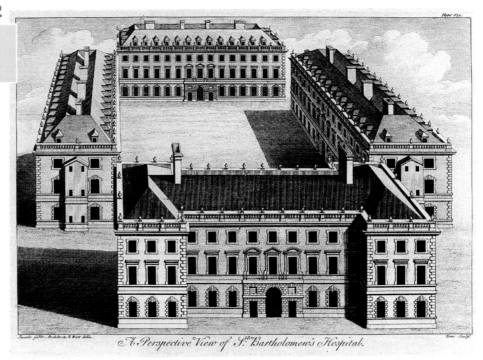

A Perspective View of St. Bartholomew's Hospital.

There was, however, still a shortage of hospitals. This became more and more obvious in an age when Britain's population was rapidly increasing. The quality of nursing was also very basic and no real progress was made until the nineteenth century.

Questions

1   'Hospitals in Britain grew steadily throughout the period 1100 to 1750.' Do you agree with this view? Give reasons.

2   When – and why – did hospitals lose their religious connection?

Unit 5 · Women and medicine

Women are sometimes ignored by historians. In the history of medicine, however, this would be difficult to do, as this Unit shows.

5.1 Gynaecology and obstetrics

There are two branches of medicine which concern women alone. One is gynaecology, which deals with diseases and disorders of women's reproductive systems. The other is obstetrics, which deals with the care and treatment of women before, during and after childbirth. They are closely connected.

What was the extent of knowledge about gynaecology and obstetrics?

Much was known about gynaecology in the Ancient World, by the Egyptians, Hebrews, Greeks and Romans. But then came a long period of regress. During the Middle Ages there were two obstacles to progress, both religious. In the West the barriers were put up by the Church, in the Arab world by Islam. In both cases, it was considered wrong for male physicians to examine female organs. This meant that female patients had to rely on other women. Because of their status in society, these women were unlikely to have any medical qualifications. There was also a general lack of interest in the study of anatomy.

It was not until the sixteenth century that progress was resumed. Books were once again published on the subject of childbirth. Eucharius Roesslin, for example, wrote *Rosegarden of Pregnant Women and Midwives* in 1513 (see Source 1) and *The Byrth of Mankind* in 1540. This included information about stools used for giving birth and about the positioning of the baby (see Source 2).

The study of gynaecology was also revived. Vesalius wrote *De Humani Corporis Fabrica* (see page 12), which included the first accurate description of the reproductive organs of the female body. Gabriel Fallopius added new knowledge by providing the first descriptions of the fallopian tubes (named after him). Britain's contributions were mainly in the eighteenth century. William Smellie, for example, wrote his *Treatise on Midwifery* in 1753 and William Hunter the *Anatomy of the Human Uterus* in 1774.

Did women benefit from this knowledge?

Very few women ever came into contact with a doctor during the sixteenth and seventeenth centuries. It was unusual for men to be in attendance at a birth. Even the astrologers called in by wealthy families

Source 1

The title page of Roesslin's book, *Rosegarden of Pregnant Women and Midwives*, 1513.

Source 2

Illustrations from Roesslin's book *The Byrth of Mankind*, 1540.

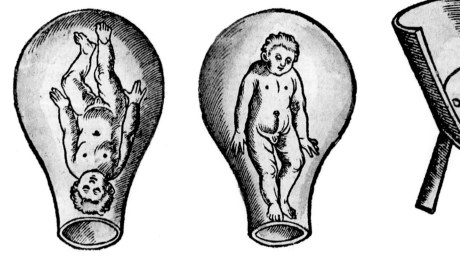 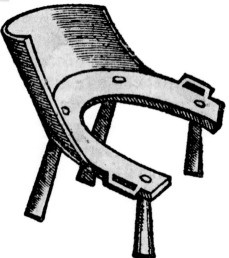

to cast the horoscope of the new baby kept their distance during the actual delivery. For most women childbirth was, before 1700, very little different from what it had been in the Middle Ages. All too often it ended in death, as many a churchyard reminds us:

Source 3

A seventeenth-century gravestone inscription.

Nineteen years a maiden,
One year a wife,
One hour a mother
And so I lost my life.

During the eighteenth century many changes occurred, especially in the practice of midwifery. The untrained midwife (who was nearly always a woman) was gradually being replaced by trained doctors, who called themselves *accoucheurs* and knew something about anatomy. They might have attended a course on midwifery run by William Smellie in Edinburgh or by William Hunter in London. They were trained when to let nature take its course and when to assist the delivery. If necessary, they would use forceps (see Source 4). Women were encouraged to go to hospital to give birth rather than stay at home.

Source 4

Obstetric instruments used in the eighteenth century.

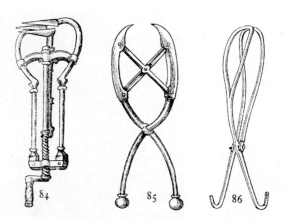

These changes did not necessarily bring improvements. The new accoucheurs were too fond of using their instruments and often committed great damage, both to the mother and to the baby. In any case, the instruments were never sterilised, and rarely washed. They were therefore likely to spread infection and sepsis. There were several epidemics of childbed, or puerperal, fever, which had been rare earlier. This was probably due to the growing use of instruments and to unhygienic conditions in hospitals, where fever could spread. There was no progress in dealing with pain during delivery, or with post-birth shock. Thus the number of deaths remained remarkably high and solutions to these problems were not really forthcoming until well into the nineteenth century.

Questions

1 How effectively does Source 3 show the dangers of childbirth during the period?

2 'The increase in male midwives placed women in greater danger during childbirth.' Do you agree with this?

5.2 Women as practitioners

Women played a vitally important part in medicine although, by and large, they did not have any medical qualification. They fulfilled two roles – as midwives and as healers.

How important were women as midwives and healers?

Midwives

During the Middle Ages and before about 1700, midwives were always women. They might be well known within the local community for their skills, or they might help out occasionally when needed.

Source 1

This woodcut shows midwives attending a birth in the sixteenth century.

In some cases, women from the upper classes might develop an interest in midwifery; Lady Hoby was a sixteenth-century example:

Source 2

From the diary of Lady Hoby.

August 15th, 1559. In the morning at 6 o'clock I prayed privately: that done, I went to a wife in travail of child. I was busy till 1 o'clock, about which time she delivered and I having praised God returned home.

in travail of child In labour.

Healers

In a period when most people never saw a qualified physician there had to be an alternative within the local community. This was usually a local woman who was able to offer various cures and treatments. Possibly women were more at home than men with the use of herbs because they were likely to have used some of them in cooking. They might also have known about herb-based ointments.

Some of the best-known healers were women from the upper class. Again, this was connected with their domestic functions. They would have managed large households and would have developed an interest in medicine when problems such as injuries and illnesses were referred to them. We can get an idea of the importance of such people from the diary of Lady Hoby:

Source 3

From the diary of Lady Hoby.

January 30th. I dressed a poor boy's leg that came to me...[then] I dressed the hand of one of our servants that was very sore cut....After dinner I went to [Lady Limbrick] when she made me a medicine – after that I dressed one of the men's hands that was hurt.

The declining status of women in medicine
Gradually, however, the status of women in medicine declined and by 1750 there were fewer midwives and healers than there had been before 1700. There were several reasons for this.

First, women depended very much on an amateur knowledge of medicine. They filled a gap left by the ignorance of the Middle Ages and they attended to women's complaints when it was unheard of for men to do so. This began to change during the Renaissance and the Scientific Revolution of the seventeenth century. References to women's anatomy became more open and knowledge about it gradually increased. Men like Fallopius and Smellie began to specialise in it.

Second, more women in the eighteenth century were treated in hospitals. These were controlled entirely by men. The training offered by Smellie and Hunter was for men alone, even though it was intended to help women. The practical effect of this was to squeeze out many female midwives from the higher levels of society, leaving them to operate mainly at the lower levels among women who were never likely to go to hospital.

Third, men began to show more interest in the knowledge of herbs, an area which had previously been dominated by women. Female herbalists were gradually replaced by male apothecaries and pharmacologists.

Fourth, the medical profession was becoming more and more jealous of its reputation and was setting standards and qualifications (see Unit 4). From these, women were automatically excluded.

Fifth, there was a strong social reason for discrimination against women. Their role was seen as one of childbearing and home-care. This also affected the way in which men saw women as mentally and physically incapable of carrying out medical work.

For all these reasons, an obvious area for women's involvement in medicine was not taken up in the eighteenth century. The growth of hospitals increased the demand for nurses – but these were recruited from men. It was not until the mid-century that changes were made here.

Questions

1 a What does Unit 5 tell you about the different roles of men and women in helping mothers to give birth?
   b How and why did these roles change in the seventeenth and eighteenth centuries?

2 Why were there so few women midwives or nurses in eighteenth-century hospitals?

Unit 6 · Disease and epidemics

6.1 The behaviour of diseases

Diseases followed very different patterns during this period. Some arrived suddenly. Others disappeared. Others again took a hold and survived for a long period. They all had one thing in common: they brought terror. Everyone was vulnerable and there was no guarantee of safety in wealth or social class.

New diseases

From time to time society is faced with the threat of a disease which was previously unknown. There were several new arrivals between 1450 and 1750, which behaved in very different ways.

Diseases which arrived, struck and stayed

When new continents were opened up during the Renaissance, diseases were caught by both the conquered and the conquerors. Infections spread swiftly among populations which had not experienced them before. The Spaniards, for example, carried influenza, smallpox and measles to the Indians of Central and South America, with deadly effect. In return, however, the Spaniards took back to Europe the sexually transmitted disease known as syphilis. This moved swiftly across Europe, carried by the French and Spanish in the Italian wars. It also spread across the trade routes, which is how it reached Britain. People tried various treatments, including boiling baths and mercury pills. Syphilis continued to be a major problem in Britain and Europe until the early twentieth century.

Another deadly disease was typhus fever. This probably came from trading contacts with Asia, especially India. It was spread by body lice and affected people living in close confinement, especially soldiers, sailors and prisoners. It swept through England and Europe in the first half of the seventeenth century, killing millions of people in the Thirty Years War (1618-48). It then quietened down. There were fewer epidemics, but it became endemic, or always present. In England it was particularly deadly in prisons and therefore became known as 'gaol fever'.

A disease which arrived, struck and disappeared

A new epidemic appeared in England in 1485 with the armies of Henry Tudor. This was the sweating sickness. During Henry VIII's reign more people died of this disease than had been killed in the Wars of the Roses. Then, mysteriously, it disappeared after a final strike in 1551, and never returned. What was it? According to one medical historian:

Source 1

Paul Hastings, *Medicine: An International History*, 1974.

Its nature has never been satisfactorily explained. Probably it was a virus infection allied with rheumatic fever and associated with lack of personal cleanliness.

Old diseases

Not all the diseases which struck Britain and Europe in the 300 years after 1450 were new. Some were old enemies, going back to the Middle Ages, or even the Ancient World. Again their course was unpredictable.

A disease which was wiped out for ever

One of the great terrors of ancient Rome had been leprosy, a disease which wasted the flesh, caused great sores and often resulted in the loss of limbs. Medieval Europe had been full of leper colonies and lazar houses, so that people suffering from leprosy could be kept isolated.

Then, from the fourteenth century onwards, the number of lepers suddenly declined. By the sixteenth century, leprosy had become so rare in Britain that most of the lazar houses had been closed down or turned to other uses. Perhaps the main reason for this change was that lepers were especially vulnerable to other diseases.

A disease which struck again, then disappeared

The greatest killer of the Middle Ages had been bubonic plague. This behaved in strange ways. In the fifteenth and early sixteenth centuries it left Britain and Europe alone. But it returned with a vengeance in the seventeenth century. The Great Plague of London killed 70,000 people in 1665. The people of London experienced again all the horrors of the Black Death of 300 years before. But this was the last epidemic of this disease that they were to suffer. The plague struck again at the French port of Marseilles in 1720, killing 50,000 people. Then it disappeared. This is one of the great mysteries of modern history. Why did it suddenly stop? Historians have suggested several reasons.

One is the **environmental theory**: that living conditions improved as a result of new buildings. This theory is often applied to London, which was largely rebuilt after being destroyed in the Great Fire of 1666. Greater use of brick and stone meant less thatch, in which rats tended to live. This increased the distance between rats and humans and made it more difficult for the plague-carrying flea to make contact.

Other historians favour the **ecological theory**. This maintains that the black rat was killed off throughout large parts of Europe, including Britain, by the brown rat. The brown rat preferred to keep its distance from humans, and, in any case, carried a different type of flea.

Some historians are not convinced by either of these explanations. They argue that much of the plague spread directly from human to human. It therefore made little difference whether the brown rat had replaced the black rat. Also, the rebuilding was no greater at the end of the seventeenth century than it had been earlier, and the streets were as filthy as ever. Besides, the black rat still lived in London and the ports. A zoologist, Graham Twigg, believes that the Black Death and its successors could not have been caused by rats at all and that historians continue to believe this against all the evidence:

Source 2

Graham Twigg, *The Black Death: A Biological Reappraisal*, 1984.

Scientists were more ready to consider it [that the plague was probably not bubonic or spread by rats] than historians, who have a fixed view and do not want to change it.

A disease which returned in a new form – and stayed

As the plague departed, a new disease took its place as the major killer in Europe and Britain. This was smallpox. There had been various outbreaks in the Middle Ages, although sometimes it was confused with measles and was in a mild form. There were three types: *variola major*, the most deadly; *variola minor*, a less serious form, and cowpox. What seems to have happened is that the more serious *variola major* took over, possibly brought to Europe from Asia as a result of the voyages of discovery. During the seventeenth century smallpox in Britain gradually increased and in the eighteenth century it became the most deadly of all diseases, especially for children.

Questions

1 Give an example of:
a how one disease wiped another out, and
b how, as one disease declined, another took its place.
Why do you think (a) and (b) happened?

2 Why do historians disagree about the reasons for the departure of plague from Britain and Europe? Does their disagreement mean that some of them must be wrong?

3 Study Sources A to F and answer the questions which follow.

Source A

The Great Plague of London, from a broadsheet of 1665.

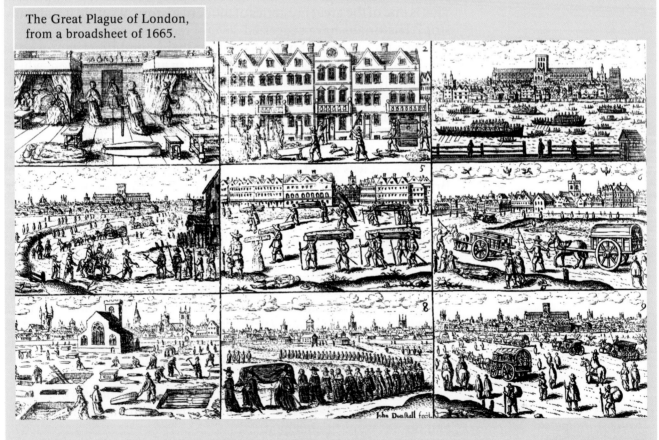

Source B

An extract from the diary of Samuel Pepys, 7 June 1665.

This day much against my will, I did in Drury Lane see two or three houses marked with a red cross upon the doors and 'Lord have mercy upon us!' writ there, which was a sad sight to me.

Source C

Some examples of deaths caused by plague in Europe in the seventeenth and early eighteenth centuries.

1603	Moscow	120,000 deaths
1630	Milan	80,000
1665	London	70,000
1679	Vienna	70,000
1681	Prague	83,000
1720	Marseilles	50,000

Source D

Vernon Coleman, *The Story of Medicine*, 1985.

Some historians argue that the plague was transmitted by fleas which lived on the black rat and that it disappeared when the black rat was driven out of Europe by the brown rat, which has a different flea and does not live so close to human beings....We shall probably never know why the plague finally died away.

Source E

A photograph of a black rat, *Rattus rattus* (left) and a brown rat, *Rattus norvegicus* (right).

Source F

Paul Hastings, *Medicine: An International History*, 1974.

...general medical practice remained largely medieval. Bleeding was still of paramount importance. Sufferers of all ages were bled for fevers, infectious diseases, and even toothache. One French surgeon bled his long-suffering patient sixty-four times in eight months.

a   What can you learn from Source A about how the plague affected London in 1665?

b   British studies on bubonic plague tend to concentrate on the Great Plague of London (1665). Does Source C suggest they are right?

c   What does Source F show about people's knowledge at the time about what caused the plague?

d   To what extent does Source E support what is said in Source D?

e   Using your own knowledge, what other theories – not mentioned in Sources A–F – have been advanced for the disappearance of bubonic plague from Britain and Europe?

f   Why do historians disagree on the reason for the disappearance of bubonic plague?

Unit 7 · Alternative medicine

During the period 1450–1750 most people experienced medicine not through physicians, but rather through 'alternative medicine'. This means treatment provided by people who had no medical training. They often relied on herbal remedies and were usually quite genuine in their desire to help. At times, however, fraudulent or dishonest cures were offered by 'quacks'.

7.1 Herbal remedies

Ever since the time of the Ancient World people had tried out plants and herbs as medical cures. There was therefore a huge range available. The most common were as follows:

Source 1

John Camp, *Magic, Myth and Medicine*, 1973.

Plant	Used as treatment for
Angelica	coughs and colds
Broom	kidney and bladder infections
Dandelion	kidney and liver disorders
Dock	skin rashes
Hyssop	stomach complaints
Lily of the valley	heart conditions
Male fern	tapeworms
Marigold	bee stings, inflammation of the eyes
Motherwort	female disorders
Nettles	nosebleed
Parsley	kidney disease
Thyme	whooping cough

How important were herbal remedies?

There are two ways of answering this question. On the one hand, herbs were a home-based remedy, used by ordinary people who would not have been able to afford treatment by a physician. This had always been the case and so we can see continuity with the past. On the other hand, herbs became a vitally important part of medicine, taken more and more seriously by experts. Here we see evidence of change.

Herbs as home-based remedies
Treatments for various illnesses or injuries were built up over many years, often by women in the local community (see Unit 5). Almost everyone took them for granted and some people even criticised more advanced methods. John Wesley, the Methodist leader, made his own preferences quite clear:

Source 2

John Wesley, *Primitive Physick: Or an Easy and Natural Method of Curing most Diseases*, 1752.

compounding Mixing.
apothecary Chemist.
distemper Illness.

And against the greater part of these medicines there is a further Objection: They consist of too many Ingredients. This common method of compounding and decompounding medicines can never be reconciled with Common Sense. Experience shows that One Thing will cure most disorders at least as twenty put together. Then why do you add the other nineteen? Only to swell the Apothecary's bill: Nay, possibly on purpose to prolong the distemper, that the Doctor and he may divide the Spoil.

Herbs and medical science

The spread of knowledge about herbs was made easier by the introduction of printing. During the sixteenth and seventeenth centuries, many books were published about particular herbs and their healing qualities. Among the earliest of these was *The Great Herbal*, printed in 1526. Other contributions followed. John Gerard published a three-volume book called *Herbal*, which is still used today as a work of reference. Nicholas Culpeper wrote *A Physical Dictionary* in 1649 and John Parkinson his *Herbal* in 1629.

Many of the early herbalists were also gardeners. This certainly applied to John Gerard, who was head gardener to the Cecil family. Such gardens were, however, private property belonging to great nobles of the day. Gradually a new idea developed, which was that gardens should be set up especially for medical research. One is particularly well known – the Oxford University Botanical Gardens.

Source 3

The Oxford University Botanical Gardens.

Herbs also featured in pharmacology, or the science of drugs. Some herbs were used as cures for specific diseases. One of the earliest remedies for a specific illness was quinine, which came from cinchona bark brought back from South America. Another drug was laudanum, extracted by Thomas Sydenham in 1660 from the opium poppy. There is, in fact, a common heritage between modern medicine and the herbal studies of earlier periods. This is because many modern drugs are extracts from particular plants, refined to produce the desired quantities and concentration.

7.2 Quacks

A quack has been defined as a person who has no medical training but pretends to offer cures and remedies. Quacks should be distinguished from ordinary practitioners who were not trained in medicine but who did a valuable job in helping people in the way they knew best:

Source 1

Roderick McGrew,
Encyclopaedia of Medical History, 1985.

What distinguishes the quack is the determination to gull and mislead the unwary for personal gain....Quackery specializes in simple answers to difficult problems, promising immediate relief for bothersome symptoms and a miraculous cure.

Who were they?

Quacks came from all over Europe (see Source 2). The eighteenth century is often known as 'the golden age of quackery', with Britain having the largest number and France not far behind.

Source 2

An advertisement for a quack from Germany.

Doctor FREDERICK,
Lately come from *Germany*.

BEGS leave to acquaint the Publick, that he undertakes to Cure the Gout, and Rheumatifm, without any return; being the firſt perſon that ever could Cure the Gout in *London*; Likewiſe, Cures the yellow Jaundice, Stitching in the Side. He likewiſe Cures any Body who is bit by a Mad Dog: Gentlemen and Ladies, I call myſelf Maſter; in a Word if you will make Trial where the Public may find great Benefit.   No Cure no Pay.

Direct to me at Mr. *Compton's*, the *Crown* and *Feathers*; in *Holbourn*, near *Red Lyon Street*, LONDON.

Source 3

A quack at a fair. This is a watercolour by Thomas Rowlandson (1756–1827).

Some moved around the country, selling their products at fairs (Source 3). Most were careful not to stay in the same place too long.

They would sell a wide range of remedies, for any disease under the sun. A particular type of quack was the 'piss-prophet'. He claimed to be able to tell all there was to know about a patient merely by looking at a urine specimen in a bottle. Usually he found out information about a patient by other means. He then amazed the patient by the knowledge he claimed to have got from the urine, and charged a huge sum for a cure.

A famous quack of the seventeenth century was Thomas Saffold, who advertised his pills in verse:

Source 4

An advertisement for pills.

It's Saffold's pills, much better than the rest,
Deservedly have got the name of Best.

Another example was Dr Case, who also used advertisements:

Source 5

A seventeenth-century advertisement.

Read judge and try
And if you die
Never believe me more!

In the eighteenth century there was William Read. Originally a tailor, he preferred to claim that he was an eye specialist. He was so successful that he was even knighted by Queen Anne. Joshua Ward was originally a politician but went over to preparing and selling powders, pills and medicines, including 'liquid sweat'. He was remarkably successful and was consulted by some of the leading politicians and writers of the time, including the Prime Minister, Sir Robert Walpole. Joanna Stevens concocted a remedy for bladder stones, consisting of carrot seeds, honey, soap, egg shells and snails. She sold this for £5,000 voted by Parliament – and then wisely disappeared when the ingredients became known.

The greatest rogue of all was James Graham, who gave electrical treatment and mudbaths. He was famed for his special bed (see Source 6), for which he charged anything between £50 and £500 per night.

Source 6

James Graham's description of his medical bed.

The Grand Celestial Bed, whose magical influences are now celebrated from pole to pole and from the rising to the setting of the sun, is 12ft long by 9ft wide, supported by forty pillars of brilliant glass of the most exquisite workmanship, in richly variegated colours.

The bed had a 'super-celestial dome' surmounted by 'exquisite figures of Cupid and Psyche'. The pillars were carved musical instruments and the whole bed was surrounded by spices and 'brilliant panes of looking glass'.

Some views on the activities of the quacks

There were many warnings during the eighteenth century about the activities of quacks, usually from the medical profession, who feared them as rivals:

Source 7

A warning against quacks from an eighteenth-century book, *Medical Imposters*.

Whoever hangs out a piss-pot for his standard, pretends upon sight of your water to tell you infirmities and directs medicine without seeing the sick person, believe them not. They are cheats: not only for the sixpence or shilling for what they call casting your urine (which much better would be cast in their faces), but for drawing you in with some fearful story of your danger and make you take a packet with you of their stuff.

Some modern historians, however, believe that the popularity of quacks can easily be explained:

Source 8

Vernon Coleman, *The Story of Medicine*, 1985.

It would be a great mistake to dismiss all these unqualified practitioners merely as grasping charlatans, for they could only get away with selling their unproven cures because the qualified practitioners had nothing better to offer. If the physicians, surgeons and apothecaries had been able to provide effective and safe forms of treatment, the quacks would not have flourished.

Some historians even go so far as to doubt that there was all that much difference between medicine and quackery:

Source 9

John Camp, *Magic, Myth and Medicine*, 1973.

This demonstrates the very thin borderline between quackery and legitimate medicine. A quack might sell a product which actually did some good, while a qualified physician sold a cure under his own name of only doubtful value. Which, then, was the quack?

Questions

(These cover both 7.1 and 7.2.)

1 'All untrained people attempting to practise medicine were frauds.' Do you agree with this? Explain your answer.

2 How might most people in 1750 try to get treatment for an illness or an injury?

3 a Why do you think most quacks were nearly always on the move?
   b Why were the more famous quacks like James Graham the exception?

4 Does Wesley (Source 2, page 37) appear to have made a distinction between quacks and genuine medical practitioners?

5 Write a conversation about healing between John Wesley and James Graham.

6 Compare Sources 4 and 5 as advertisements. Which do you think would be more likely to appeal to the people of the time?

7 In what ways do Sources 8 and 9 agree and in what ways do they disagree?

8 Source 7 was written at the time. Is it more likely than Sources 8 and 9 to be an accurate view of quacks? Give reasons for your view.

Joseph Lister in a ward
of King's College Hospital,
1890.

This photograph shows Joseph Lister, a leading surgeon, in one of the wards of King's College Hospital, London, in the late nineteenth century. It is a scene which is in some ways similar to that on page 10. Because it is a photograph, however, the details of the composition are very different from the illustration for the book by Paracelsus. What are these similarities and differences?

Three hundred and fifty years separate the two pictures and the scenes they contain, years in which many changes occurred. This applies especially to the period 1750–1900 – when many major problems in medicine were tackled and eventually resolved. Unit 8 deals with the introduction of vaccination and with the development of germ theories. Unit 9 shows how the crisis caused by cholera epidemics brought about new attitudes to public health. Unit 10 examines the way in which the problems of pain and infection in surgery were met. The revolution in nursing is covered in Unit 11 and improvements in medical training, including the qualification of women, in Unit 12.

Unit 8 · Vaccination and germ theories

Between 1750 and 1900 there was a dramatic increase in knowledge about germs and a greater understanding of how diseases are caught and spread. The most important part of this was the development of vaccines. But this took place in a rather illogical way.

Stage 1 During the seventeenth and eighteenth centuries there was no real understanding of germs, but some people were familiar with *inoculation*; they knew that catching a mild form of smallpox prevented a major attack later.

Stage 2 Then came a new development. This was a different method of preventing smallpox, used by Edward Jenner and called *vaccination*. But this idea applied only to smallpox and nothing was learned from it about the behaviour of germs.

Stage 3 Various theories about germs developed during the nineteenth century until new processes of inoculation were developed by Louis Pasteur and Robert Koch. These are more accurately called *immunisation*.

8.1 Smallpox, Jenner and vaccination

Smallpox was the greatest killer at the beginning of the nineteenth century. During the seventeenth and eighteenth centuries, it has been estimated, some 30 per cent of children in England died of it before reaching the age of three. Increasingly, people put their hope of escaping smallpox in *inoculation*. This worked in two ways. Children might be encouraged to go into the sickroom of a patient recovering from smallpox to catch a milder form of the disease. Alternatively, pus from a smallpox scab, again from a patient who was recovering, might be rubbed into an open cut. These methods worked in some cases, but often resulted in death. They were therefore very risky and extremely difficult to control. They did, however, prepare people to accept vaccination when it was introduced at the end of the eighteenth century.

What was the contribution of Edward Jenner?

A country physician, Edward Jenner (1749–1823) is best known as the man who developed a safe means of preventing smallpox – by vaccination.

Jenner observed that milkmaids who caught the mild disease of cowpox never appeared to develop smallpox. In 1796 he inoculated a small boy with cowpox and then, six weeks later, with smallpox. The boy suffered no ill-effects. In 1798 he published his main work, *An Inquiry into the Causes and Effects of Variolae Vaccinae*. In this he

Source 1

A portrait of Edward Jenner by J. Northcote (1803).

distinguished between the old practice of inoculation and what he had done by using the term *vaccination* (from the Latin *vaccinus* which means from a cow).

It has to be said that Jenner was not the first person to use cowpox as a vaccine against smallpox. A farmer near Yeovil, called Benjamin Jesty, had done the same to his wife and two sons to prevent them from catching smallpox. But because he was a farmer and not a qualified doctor he took no measures to publicise his experiment. It needed a more systematic approach by someone trained in medicine to take advantage of Jesty's ideas. In 1789 a Dr Trowbridge heard of Jesty's experiment and tried it out on his own sons, who also avoided smallpox. However, Trowbridge took no steps to follow this up.

This shows that it is rare for one person alone to be associated with a particular discovery. What really matters, however, is the willingness to persevere and to publicise the work done. Jenner did this in his writings. He was also much more active than the others had been. He vaccinated as many people as he could with cowpox, and no one suffered a serious reaction.

How effective was vaccination?

People's views

Jenner's ideas and experiments met with a mixed reaction. They were sometimes welcomed more abroad than in Britain. In France, Napoleon immediately saw the importance of the discovery and had his armies compulsorily vaccinated. The Spanish settlers did the same to their labourers in Central and South America.

In Britain there was some resistance. The Royal Society decided against publishing Jenner's findings, mainly because he was a country doctor and not a great name at the time. Some people saw vaccination as an interference with nature. There was something repulsive about taking pus from a sick cow and putting it into a human through cuts in the arm. Besides, no one could explain exactly how vaccination worked, and any success was often put down to coincidence (especially by doctors who made money through the older practice of inoculation). Compulsory vaccination was also seen as being against human rights. Herbert Spencer, an English philosopher, said that he 'detested' it.

The vaccination programme
The government ignored Spencer's view and, in 1840, made vaccination compulsory. This followed a smallpox epidemic in which 41,000 people died. The result was that smallpox declined for most of the nineteenth century, so that by 1900 it had almost disappeared. This was a major step forward in controlling disease. It was also the first example of the government accepting responsibility for an area of public health.

Questions

Study Sources A to H and answer the questions which follow.

Source A

From the diary of *John Evelyn*, 13 September 1685.

Whilst supper was making ready, I went and made a visit to Mrs Graham....Her eldest son was now sick there of the small-pox, but in a likely way to recover, and other of her children ran about among the infected, which she said she let them do on purpose that they might whilst young pass that fatal disease she fancied they were to undergo one time or other.

Source B

From a poor-house accounts book in the parish of Fitzhead, Somerset, 21 May 1769.

1769	Paid for inoculating the parish	01. 15. 00
1789	Paid Dr Cromer his bill for inoculating 27 poor people, due last year	05. 08. 00
1796	Paid Mr Sully for inocklating Thirty Four children	08. 10. 00
1798	Towards Inocklating Stook and Stones children	00. 15. 00
1798	Paid for inocklating Wm Crewse three children	00. 07. 06

Source C

Lois N. Magner, *A History of Medicine,* 1992.

Although inoculation probably had a limited impact on the overall incidence of smallpox, inoculation paved the way for the rapid acceptance of...vaccination.

Source D

Edward Jenner, *On the Cow Pox. The Original Paper,* 1796.

I selected a healthy boy about eight years old for the purpose of inoculation with the smallpox. The matter was taken from a suppurated sore on the hand of a dairy Maid who was infected by her master's Cows, and it was inserted on the 14th of May 1796, into the arms of the Boy, by means of two superficial incisions, each about three quarters of an inch long....On the 1st of July following this Boy was inoculated with Matter immediately taken from a smallpox Pustule. Several punctures and slight incisions were made in both his arms, and the matter was well rubb'd into them, but no disease follow'd.

Source E

Jenner's drawing of the cowpox lesion he used to develop his vaccine.

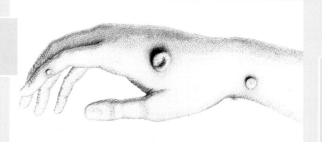

Source F

Deaths from smallpox in Birmingham.

1871–1880: 1,042
1881–1890:   204
1891–1900:   253
1901–1910:   1

Source G

F. Cartwright, *A Social History of Medicine*, 1977.

Jenner's introduction of vaccination stands as one of the most beneficial changes in the history of social medicine. He did not know the cause of disease but his work is recognised as the starting point of attempts to combat infection by immunization.

Source H

Robert P. Hudson, *Disease and its Control: The Shaping of Modern Thought*, 1983.

In truth Jenner's lead turned out to be a cul-de-sac. His discovery depended on a natural fluke of sorts, on the fact that a virus that caused a relatively [harmless] human disease, cowpox, provided cross-immunity to the deadly smallpox.

Questions

1 Using Sources A, B, D and E and your own knowledge, explain the difference between inoculation and vaccination.

2 Show how Sources D and E would have a different value for people wanting to spread vaccination in the nineteenth century and historians today enquiring into the development of vaccination.

3 Use any of the other sources, and your own knowledge, to say whether you agree with Lois Magner in Source C, (a) that inoculation had 'a limited impact' on smallpox, and (b) that inoculation 'paved the way for the rapid acceptance of...vaccination'.

4 a Does Source F show that smallpox was steadily reduced in Birmingham during the nineteenth century?
   b What other statistics are needed to evaluate Source F fully?

5 'The fact that Sources G and H differ in their views of Jenner's importance means that one is right and the other wrong.' Do the other Sources and your own knowledge show this to be the case?

6 Are historians today in a better position than people alive at the time to judge the progress made in the nineteenth century in inoculation?

8.2 Germ theories, Pasteur and Koch

Was vaccination a dead end?

Normally, one would expect a discovery as important as vaccination to have led rapidly to similar developments with many other diseases. But this did not happen. We have already seen the view of one historian that vaccination was a cul-de-sac or dead end. This is, of course, controversial, but it is certainly true that there was no other disease which acted in the same way as cowpox did to smallpox. This meant that there had to be a return to the earlier idea of inoculation when dealing with diseases other than smallpox. Before this could be done, however, more knowledge was needed about the methods of infection.

Theories of disease and infection

The idea of germs existed before the nineteenth century. A major theoretical advance was made by Hieronymus Fracastorius (1483–1553), who is sometimes known as the 'first epidemiologist'. His main work was *De contagione* (or *Infection*). He argued that infection could be passed on in three ways. One was through direct personal contact, another through clothing and utensils, and a third at a distance. He also believed that there were minute particles which were responsible for the spread of disease. Unfortunately, his views were premature and it was to be another three centuries before they were taken up, or rather re-invented. This shows that sometimes brilliant ideas fail to break through in practice.

Then, during the nineteenth century, two theories emerged about the way in which these minute particles behaved. One was that they were spread by miasma, or infectious mist. Decaying matter, it was believed, mixed with the air and poisoned it so that people caught a variety of infections from it. This was widely believed by physicians to be the cause of most diseases. The miasma theory was challenged by the so-called contagionists. The professor of anatomy at Zurich, Jacob Henlé (1809–95), wrote *On Miasmata and Contagia*, in which he argued strongly against miasma. He said that no one had ever proved its existence. Organisms, on the other hand, clearly multiplied inside the infected person, which meant that they must be *living* organisms.

Source 1

Louis Pasteur, a portrait by Albert-Gustaf Edelfelt.

Hence the most logical cause of illness was germs from a sick individual. These might be expelled by the lungs into the air or be excreted through the intestines into water. Henlé's point was proved by Pasteur and Koch, who applied the germ theory to specific diseases.

The contribution of Louis Pasteur

Pasteur was a French chemist, who developed a theory that germs multiplied through fermentation. This could take place inside or, in certain conditions, outside the body.

He is remembered particularly for two contributions. One was the destruction of germs in liquids through a process of slow heating, known as *pasteurisation*. This was very appropriate for milk and reduced the number of cases of glandular tuberculosis.

His other contribution was immunisation against several deadly diseases. Working with cholera in chickens, he found that a cholera virus he had produced and then allowed to remain over the summer failed to kill chickens. When the same chickens were then infected with new cholera virus, nothing happened. The theory of weakening a virus by heating or cooling and then using it to develop immunity was therefore born. Unfortunately, this could not be applied to human cholera, but it did work for anthrax. Even more important was the success he had in producing in 1885 a serum for rabies, probably the most horrible of all diseases. This was carried out through a series of injections, using the rabies virus in several stages of weakness. Pasteur's work was continued in a specially built laboratory called the Pasteur Institute. His contributions to germ theory were to prove vitally important in the development of antiseptics by Joseph Lister (see pages 64–5).

The contribution of Robert Koch

Koch (1843–1910) was a German physician. His most important contribution was to develop pure strains of various diseases, starting with anthrax. He is therefore associated with the beginning of the science of microbiology. He also made it possible to stain bacteria so that they could be identified by colour coding.

His most promising achievement was to identify the microbe responsible for tuberculosis. He claimed to have discovered a cure in the form of tuberculin. Unfortunately, this was not very effective and the cure had to wait until the twentieth century (see page 82).

Questions

1 Pasteur once said that luck and hard work go together: 'in the fields of observation chance favours only the mind which is prepared'. Is this true (a) of his own work and (b) of the work of Jenner and Koch? Explain your answers.

2 a Why can vaccination be described as a 'cul-de-sac', or dead end?
  b Explain why you agree or disagree with this description.

3 a What did Pasteur add to Henlé's work on germs?
  b What did Koch add to Pasteur's work?

Unit 9 · The public health crisis

In Unit 8 we saw the government accepting responsibility for doing something about smallpox by making vaccination compulsory. During the nineteenth century there were two other diseases which were as dreadful as smallpox and which also presented a challenge to the government. One was tuberculosis; the other was cholera. These were more difficult to tackle than smallpox. There was no instant vaccination because both diseases spread as a result of poor living conditions. Any action by the state was therefore much more involved – and expensive – than for smallpox. This was because it had to look at people's living conditions as well as at the diseases themselves. The state was forced to take on more responsibility for public health than at any time since the days of the Roman Empire fifteen hundred years earlier.

9.1 The problem of poor living conditions

Between 1750 and 1850, Britain went through an industrial revolution. In many ways this brought great progress: new industries, increased wealth, better farming methods and new forms of transport, such as the railways. There was also a huge change in living conditions. The towns increased rapidly in population, as Source 1 shows:

Source 1

Official census figures showing the growth of population in five cities.

	1801	1851
London	1,100,000	2,600,000
Birmingham	70,000	220,000
Leeds	53,000	170,000
Manchester	75,000	450,000
Sheffield	46,000	135,000

Larger cities were a necessary result of industrialisation. But they brought conditions which were in many ways regressive. The quality of the environment deteriorated rapidly because more people were concentrated in the towns. The worst problems concerned water pollution and living conditions. Sources 2–4 are typical examples of pollution, and Sources 5–8 show the squalor in which many people lived.

Source 2

An extract, written by Dr Southwood-Smith, from the *Report of the Commissioners* (1838). This describes Lamb's Fields in London.

privies Toilets.

An open area, of about 700 feet in length, and 300 feet in width; of this space about 300 feet are constantly covered by stagnant water, winter and summer. In the area thus submerged there is always a quantity of putrefying animal and vegetable matter, the odour of which at the present moment is most offensive. An open filthy ditch encircles this place...[into which] the privies of all the houses of a street called North-street open: these privies are completely uncovered, and the soil from them is allowed to accumulate in the open ditch.

Source 3

A description of Manchester, by Charles Reade.

Perhaps the most hideous town in creation. All ups and downs and back slums. Massive volumes of black smoke veil the sun and the blue sky even on the brightest day. More than one crystal stream runs sparkling down the valleys, and enters the town; but they soon get defiled, and creep through it heavily charged with dyes, clogged with putridity, and bubbling with poisonous gases.

Source 4

An extract from 'Pride of London', *Punch*, 1852.

Know ye the stream where the cesspool and sewer
Are emptied of all their foul slushes and slimes
Where the gas-works rain down the blackest of soot
Where the air's filled with smells that no nose can define,
And the banks team prolific with corpses canine.

Source 5

A street scene in a London slum.

Source 6

Dwellings of Manchester operatives (1862).

Source 7

An extract from Dr Neil Arnott's account of Glasgow slums, *Parliamentary Papers*, 1842.

There are no privies or drains there, and the dungheaps received all the filth which the swarm of wretched inhabitants could give....The interiors of these houses and their inmates correspond with their exteriors. We saw half-dressed wretches, crowding together to be warm; and in one bed, although in the middle of the day, several women were imprisoned under a blanket, because so many others had on their backs all the articles of dress that belonged to the party who were then out of doors on the streets.

How did these conditions affect health?

Two diseases came to be associated specifically with water pollution and bad living conditions; tuberculosis and cholera.

Tuberculosis

This existed in two forms. One was caused, mainly in children, by drinking the milk of infected cows; this was 'bovine tuberculosis' or 'scrofula'. The other, often called 'consumption', attacked the lungs. The first mainly affected the countryside, but the second took hold as the towns grew with the Industrial Revolution. It took over from smallpox during the nineteenth century as the greatest of the regular killer diseases.

Cholera

Cholera was a recent import into Britain; in fact, it was unknown before 1831. It is believed to have come from central India, where it had been endemic for thousands of years. From there it had spread to China, then across the trade routes to Europe. It was more unpredictable than tuberculosis, striking from time to time in the form of epidemics. The worst of these were in 1831, 1848, 1853 and 1866. The patient usually died, since there was no effective treatment.

Source 8

Symptoms of cholera, by a contemporary.

Vomiting or diarrhoea come on; the eyes sink; the lips, face, neck, hands, thighs and the whole surface become a leaden blue, purple, black or deep brown; the pulse becomes weak. The skin is deadly cold, the tongue flabby and chilled like a piece of dead fish. The patient struggles for breath.

Understandably, the great cholera epidemics of the nineteenth century caused panic, which must have been similar to the fear, in earlier times, of bubonic plague.

Questions

1 Source 2 comes from an official report, Source 3 from a private observer and Source 4 from a humorous magazine. How do they differ and what do they have in common?

2 How might Sources 1 and 7 be used by
   a people wanting health improvements in the nineteenth century, and
   b historians today studying public health developments in the nineteenth century?

9.2 The debate

The panic during the cholera epidemics made people debate a number of key issues. First, what was the cause of cholera? And second, whose responsibility was public health?

What was the cause of cholera?

As we have seen in Unit 8, there was a major controversy between the 'miasmatists' and 'contagionists' about the spread of disease. The contagionists were convinced that cholera was spread by personal contact – via the person or clothes or bedding. The miasmatists believed that it was carried through the air, something like an infectious mist.

At first, many people followed the miasma approach. A report in 1842 stated that

Source 1

Report of the Sanitary Condition of the Labouring Population, 1842.

the various forms of epidemic...are caused, or aggravated...chiefly among the labouring class by atmospheric impurities produced by decomposing animal and vegetable substances, by damp and filth, and close and overcrowded dwellings.

It was not until the 1850s that cholera was connected with polluted water. In 1854 John Snow, a young doctor, proved a connection between 500 cholera cases and a water pump in the Broad Street area of London. People nearby using water from another source did not catch the disease. He also proved that the pumps which drew their water from the down-river flow of the Thames were more likely to produce

Source 2

A *Punch* cartoon of 1858, 'The silent highwayman'.

cholera than those which drew from the part of the Thames which was up-river of the city. Once the pump was put out of action there were no new cases of cholera – apparently conclusive proof that the disease was transmitted through infected water.

The cholera virus took some time to identify. Louis Pasteur had proved the existence of bacteria, but the work of Koch and Pierre Roux, a pupil of Pasteur, established the precise cause of cholera: the virus passes via the faeces of one person to the stomach of another.

Once the connection between cholera and polluted water had been demonstrated, there was a great deal of publicity. Even *Punch*, a humorous magazine, joined in the debate (Source 2).

The strange thing about all this was that tuberculosis, which killed many more people than cholera, attracted far less interest. This was because cholera appeared in the form of epidemics, which are always likely to cause panic. Tuberculosis killed more slowly and was therefore less startling. Occasionally the type known as scrofula was mentioned, but it was always cholera which attracted the main attention. Two more *Punch* cartoons typify this (Sources 3 and 4):

DIPHTHERIA.   SCROFULA.   CHOLERA.

Source 3

A *Punch* cartoon of 1858: 'Father Thames introducing his offspring to the fair city of London'.

Source 4

A *Punch* cartoon: 'A court for King Cholera'.

Who should be responsible for public health?

The fiercest debate concerned the question of responsibility for dealing with the crisis of public health. There were particularly strong views about the role of the government.

Arguments for non-intervention

Several arguments were put forward against the state taking action to deal with matters of public health. Some people felt that the threat of cholera had been exaggerated and that it was being used for corrupt purposes:

Source 5

From a poster in Lambeth, in London (February 1832).

humbug Nonsense.

> Cholera humbug! – Inhabitants of Lambeth, be not imposed upon by the...false reports that the Asiatic cholera has reached London. A set of half-starved doctors, apothecaries' clerks and jobbers...have endeavoured to frighten the nation into a lavish expenditure.

Another argument was that government action would interfere with people's basic rights – including the freedom to be dirty:

Source 6

An extract from *The Times*, 1854.

> ...we prefer to take our chance with the cholera than be bullied into health. There is nothing a man hates so much as being cleansed against his will or having his floor swept, his halls whitewashed, his dungheaps cleared away and his thatch forced to give way to slate. It is a fact that many people have died from a good washing.

Some people believed that if the state acted to improve housing the moral courage of the poor would somehow be reduced:

Source 7

The views of Lord Shaftesbury in 1863. He was a Member of Parliament who campaigned for better working conditions and for better housing for the poor.

pauperization Making people poor.

> If the state is to be asked not only to provide houses for the labouring classes, but also to supply them at nominal rents, it will, while doing something on behalf of their physical condition, destroy their moral energies. It will, in fact, be an official proclamation that, without any efforts of their own, certain poor people shall enter into the enjoyment of many good things at the expense of others....The mischief of it would be very serious. It would, besides being a kind of legal pauperization, give a heavy blow and great discouragement to the spirit of healthy thrift now arising among the people.

Arguments for state action

Several important people put the case for action by the state. One was William Farr (1807–83), a medical expert, who assembled a huge range of statistics showing various causes of death. He strongly recommended government intervention in specific cases.

Source 8

The view of William Farr in 1843 (in a letter to the Registrar-General).

> Over the supply of water – the sewerage...the poor can have no command...and it is precisely upon these points that the Government can interfere with most advantage.

Another was Edwin Chadwick (1800–90). He was appointed Assistant Commissioner of the Poor Law Commission in 1832, and Chief Commissioner the following year. He also showed concern about the working conditions of children in factories. But his main interest was in public health and he was appointed to the Board of Health in 1848. He retired from public life in 1854 when the Board of Health was joined to the Local Government Board.

Source 9

A photograph of Edwin Chadwick.

Chadwick had several arguments. First, he longed for the day when ...

Source 10

Report of the Sanitary Condition of the Labouring Population, 1842.

induced Persuaded.

man shall be brought to acknowledge that it is by his own hand, through the neglect of a few obvious rules, that the seeds of ideas are most lavishly sown...when Governments shall be induced to consider the preservation of a nation's health an object as important as the promotion of its commerce or the maintenance of its conquests.

Chadwick also believed that people's moral habits were badly affected by such poor conditions:

Source 11

Report of the Sanitary Condition of the Labouring Population, 1842.

...the state of the conveniences...gives a very fair indication of the state of the habits of the population in respect to household, and even personal cleanliness.

Chadwick recommended that the government should take certain specific measures:

Source 12

Report of the Sanitary Condition of the Labouring Population, 1842.

The primary and most important measures are drainage, the removal of all refuse of habitations, streets, and roads, and the improvement of supplies of water.
   For the prevention of disease...it would be good economy to appoint a district medical officer independent of private practice.

A third influence was Thomas Southwood-Smith (1788–1861). Like Chadwick, he played an important part in various committees considering the problem of sanitary conditions, some of which he chaired. His views came out in the reports. He went so far as to say that improvements were impossible without state action:

Source 13

From the *Report of the Select Committee on the Health of Towns*, 1840.

There do not appear to be any practicable means of removing them [poor conditions] without legislative interference...here would seem to be a proper and legitimate field for the exercise of legislative wisdom and power.

Laissez-faire Literally translated from French, this means 'let do'. Loosely translated, it means 'do not interfere'. Here, it refers to the view that the government should interfere as little as possible in social and economic life.

The great debate on the government's role lasted for much of the nineteenth century. It centred on the meaning of the term *laissez-faire*. Almost everyone accepted that the government should take as little action that would affect people's lives as possible. Some believed this applied to everything. Others, like Farr, Chadwick and Southwood-Smith believed that it should apply to the economy only. They felt that the social effects of economic growth were so serious that *laissez-faire* should not be applied here at all. This view eventually won the day. Gradually the state became more and more involved in social issues such as public health at the very time that it was withdrawing more and more from controlling the economy.

Questions

1 Various measures were used to try to control cholera. Look at the list below and say whether each measure owed more to the ideas of the contagionists or of the miasmatists. Give reasons.
   – fumigation (using smoke to destroy pests)
   – whitewashing walls
   – burning of the clothes of the dead
   – burying victims in separate cemeteries.

2 Look at Sources 2, 3 and 4. How were these cartoons from *Punch* influenced by the debate on the causes of cholera?

3 What evidence is there in this Unit to disprove the reference to 'cholera humbug' in Source 5?

4 What arguments did Chadwick and Southwood-Smith use against the argument in Source 6?

5 Shaftesbury is normally associated with good works and factory reform. Is this completely inconsistent with the views he expressed about public health in Source 7?

9.3 The solution

Attempts to improve public health were made by the central government in London, by local authorities, and by private companies and private individuals. Which were the most effective?

Who did most to improve public health?

Central government

Central government did not have the funds to undertake large schemes of public health. This was because income tax was kept at the lowest

Source 1

A summary of government investigations into public health.

possible rate. At first, the government took the line of drawing attention to the problem and setting up bodies to investigate it.

1838	Report on some of the physical causes of sickness and mortality	Dr Southwood-Smith argued that disease was due mainly to bad sewerage which led to infected water.
1842	Enquiry into the Sanitary Condition of the Labouring Population of Great Britain	Chadwick gathered evidence from all parts of Britain to prove the connection between disease and infected water.
1844	Royal Commission on the Health of Towns	Southwood-Smith gathered further evidence to show the dehumanising effect of squalor and the evils of overcrowding.

We have already seen extracts from these reports. They fuelled the debate on what measures were needed and forced the government into the next stage of action, which was to introduce Acts of Parliament.

By the 1848 Public Health Act, local Boards of Health could be set up and Medical Officers of Health could be appointed. A General Board of Public Health was established which could force a town to introduce a Board of Health if its death rate rose above 23 in 1,000. Chadwick was made Secretary to the General Board. But the General Board did not last long. Chadwick proved to be too autocratic: that is, he tried to impose his views on the local boards. There was much opposition to his interference. His power was ended in 1854 and the General Board was ended in 1858.

From this time onwards the government adopted a mixture of measures through a series of new laws. Some of these *allowed* authorities to take certain measures. These were permissive legislation. Occasionally a law would be passed *forcing* authorities to take action: this was compulsory, or mandatory.

Source 2

A summary of legislation dealing with public health, 1858–1900.

1858	**Public Health Act**	Each town was permitted to set up a local Board of Health, but without the interference of a General Board.
1866	**Sanitary Act**	Each town was forced to appoint Sanitary Inspectors to end the worst cases of overcrowding.
1872	**Public Health Act**	Sanitary authorities were set up and the appointment of Medical Officers of Health was made compulsory.
1875	**Artisans Dwelling Act**	Local authorities were given the power to purchase and demolish slum housing.
1875	**Public Health Act**	Local authorities were given powers to enforce regulations on water supplies and sanitation. Towns were forced to appoint Health Inspectors and Sanitary Inspectors.
1890	**Housing of the Working Classes Act**	Local authorities were given the powers to build areas of new housing (known as council housing).

Action by local authorities?

Central government did not see its role as forcing through detailed changes, which fell to the local authorities. There was a wide variety of these, some doing far more than others to deal with the problems of public health.

Two cities which achieved a great deal were Birmingham and Liverpool. Both had terrible reputations in the middle of the nineteenth century. Both had improved greatly towards the end. In Birmingham there was a strong political drive by the Liberal Party under the Mayor, Joseph Chamberlain. He secured the demolition of some slum areas, the building of new sewers and the construction of Corporation Street. Liverpool had new sections of sewers built. It also had a greatly improved refuse collection service, regulations about house-building and a system of public baths.

Housing presented a real problem to all local authorities. It was easy enough to demolish slums, but who would replace them? As one medical officer in London said:

Source 3

Charity Organisation Reporter, 15 May 1874.

> My first impulse was to declare the house unfit for human habitation, and by means of a magistrate's order to remove the inhabitants at once. A moment's reflection, however, convinced me that...the poor people thus suddenly ejected would be compelled to seek shelter in dwellings more crowded and in an equally bad sanitary condition.

Local authorities were able from 1890 to build council houses (see Source 2), but very few did so, apart from London and Liverpool. Even Liverpool housed only 1.3 per cent of its population in this way. It was not until after the First World War that major slum clearance schemes were started.

Action by private enterprise?

Private enterprise had a mixed record before 1900.

On the one hand, most towns had their water supplied and controlled by private companies; there were eight of these in London alone. On the whole they tried to resist changes because these would affect their profits. London's water supplies eventually had to be taken over by the local authority until 1902.

In housing, however, many improvements were the result of private enterprise rather than state control. The most spectacular came as a result of the efforts of four industrialists who built housing for their workers in the form of 'model villages'. These had water and gas, a chapel and gymnasium, gardens and allotments. Titus Salt built over 800 houses for his workers near Bradford in the 1850s. W.H. Lever constructed Port Sunlight near Birkenhead. George Cadbury set up Bournville near Birmingham. Joseph Rowntree's contribution was New Earswick near York.

Not all improvements were done on such a large scale. Octavia Hill showed the way to more modest measures by buying up poor properties, doing them up and letting them (see Source 5).

Source 4

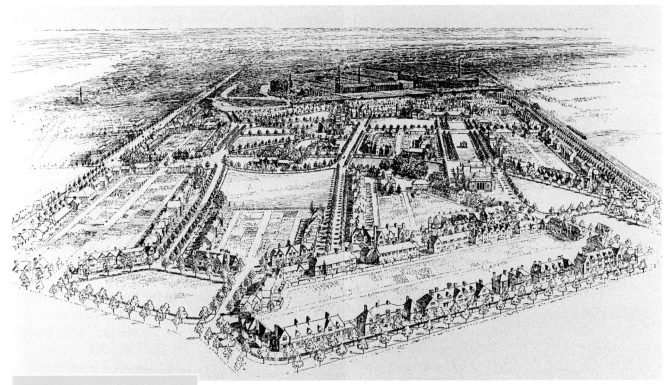

A bird's-eye view of Port Sunlight, Wirral.

Source 5

Octavia Hill's description of her housing enterprise scheme, 1875.

As soon as I entered into possession, each family had an opportunity of doing better: those who would not pay were ejected. The rooms they vacated were cleansed: the tenants who showed signs of improvement moved into them and thus, in turn, an opportunity was obtained for having each room distempered and papered. The drains were put in order...the roof, the plaster, the woodwork were repaired.

But how much could realistically be achieved by private enterprise? People like Henry Lever and Octavia Hill could do no more than scratch the surface of the problem. More had to be done by central government and local authorities, something that was recognised in the twentieth century.

Questions

1 Examine Source 2. For each of the Acts say which was permissive and which was mandatory. Give reasons for your choice.

2 Central government, local authorities and private enterprise all took action on public health. Which achieved the most in (a) water supplies and sewerage and (b) housing? Explain your views.

Unit 10 · Developments in surgery

At the beginning of the nineteenth century there were two enemies to effective surgery. One was pain during the operation; the other was infection afterwards. These were real obstacles to progress. Only when they had been dealt with was it possible to take major strides in surgery. The Victorian period saw the necessary breakthrough, as a result of the work of surgeons like Simpson and Lister.

10.1 Problems in surgery

Why was surgery so dangerous?

The operating environment

Operating theatres at the beginning of the nineteenth century would have been unrecognisable to us today. They were rarely swept and only the sand box under the operating table, used for collecting spilt blood, would be changed. Normally the room would be encrusted with filth and would smell of decay and death. Little wonder that operating theatres were often called slaughterhouses:

Source 1

A description of operating theatres by Sir Hector Cameron, a nineteenth-century surgeon.

> Every surgical ward, no matter how well ventilated, [was filled with] a foetid, stinking odour.

Surgeons wore old coats to protect their suits. These were never washed and might have on them dried blood and pus going back several years. They used ordinary string or whipcord to tie off arteries. Instruments were rarely washed. One surgeon regularly sharpened his scalpel on the sole of his boot before operating with it.

The problem of pain

An operation which would be taken for granted today would then have been the worst thing most people were ever likely to have experienced. Here is a description of a typical operation from a secondary source:

Source 2

A. J. Youngson, *The Scientific Revolution in Victorian Medicine*, 1979.

> Dragged unwillingly or carried from the ward to the operating theatre by a couple of hospital attendants the patient was laid on an operating table and if necessary strapped down, surrounded by curious strangers. The first cut of the scalpel must have caused searing pain, and few patients were able to clench their teeth and remain silent. Shriek after shriek were more likely to fill the room, ebbing away to convulsive cries and sobs as the operation proceeded.

Now an account from a primary source:

Source 3

A medical student's description of an operation on an elderly patient in 1861.

scrotum The sac containing the testicles.

> Professor Syme with a pair of scissors at once cut out the cancer which was situated on the most dependent part of the scrotum. The shouts of the old fellow were terrific. Professor Syme, after he had completed the tying of the vessel cut, questioned him concerning the period of its growth, and got for a reply: 'Hoo the devil can I answer any questions just noo?' This created a very hearty laugh among the students, which did not improve the temper of the patient.

The pain experienced by patients would have been equivalent to the worst tortures, some barely imaginable. This meant that the surgeon had to act very swiftly to prevent the patient from dying of shock. Amputations of legs or arms were often done in under a minute. A surgeon's strength was often more important than his skill. Operations to adjust broken bones were impossible because of the pain involved. Serious fractures were therefore treated by amputation.

Source 4

An operation before anaesthetics.

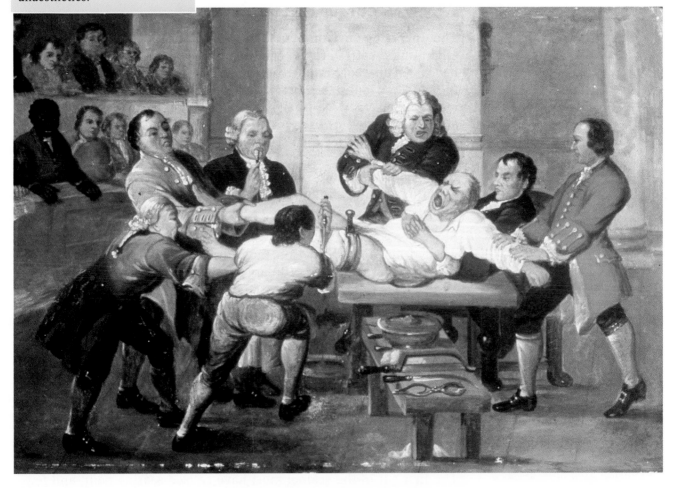

The problem of infection

The absence of sterile conditions very often led to infection and complications. The most common were septicaemia (blood poisoning) and gangrene. These led to a painful death. According to an early nineteenth-century surgeon:

Source 5

John Bell, *The Principles of Surgery*, 1801.

The pain is dreadful; the cries of the sufferers are the same in the night as in the day-time; they are exhausted in the course of a week, and die: or if they survive, and the ulcers continue to eat down and disjoin the muscles, the great vessels are at last exposed and eroded, and they bleed to death.

Questions

1 What points do Sources 2 and 3 have in common and in what ways do they differ?

2 What does Source 3 show about the attitude to pain before the regular use of anaesthetics?

10.2 Solutions

What was the answer to these problems in surgery? The breakthrough came with the development of anaesthetics and antiseptics. In both cases there had been much preliminary work.

The development of anaesthetics

There had been many early attempts to reduce the amount of pain in surgery. Paré, for example, had tried pressing on the carotid artery in the neck to make his patient unconscious. Alternatives were the use of opium or hypnotism, or putting pressure on the nerves near the site of the operation, or freezing the site with ice. The crudest was a blow to the head to make the patient unconscious – which is much more difficult to do than many films would have us believe. All of these methods had problems. They might put the patient out permanently and were hardly appropriate for women in childbirth.

Then came a period of rapid change. Some discoveries and inventions are the result of work done by many people, although one of these normally gets the credit. There was a long chain of people who made possible the type of anaesthetic which is inhaled. For example, Robert Hooke pointed out that the lungs provided air for distribution by the blood, which Harvey had proved circulated round the body (see page 17). Joseph Priestley identified oxygen as a vital gas within the air. From that stage it was realised that different gases might have their use in medicine. The next stage came with experiments by Humphrey Davy with nitrous oxide. When he inhaled it, he found that this removed the pain from a wisdom tooth. He drew an important deduction:

Source 1

Humphrey Davy, *Researches*, 1800.

As nitrous oxide...appears capable of destroying physical pain, it may probably be used with advantage during surgical operations in which no great effusion of blood takes place.

effusion Flow.

Unfortunately, this was not taken further. Davy assumed that the gas increased the flow of blood and that this would make bleeding more of a problem during operations. Other experiments followed. Henry Hill Hickman showed that mice and rats which kept re-inhaling their own breath became unconscious through carbon dioxide. But he failed to interest the medical authorities in either England or France.

The next gas tried was ether. This was used first of all during the extraction of teeth by William Morton in 1846 and then for the amputation of a leg by Robert Liston in the same year. But ether had side effects. It irritated the eyes and sometimes caused vomiting. Clearly, something else was needed.

The contribution of James Simpson

The real breakthrough came with the work of James Simpson (1811–70), Professor of Midwifery at Edinburgh. He wrote numerous articles on infections and midwifery. But his main interest was in attempting to dull the pain during childbirth. He tried sulphuric ether, about which he had heard a great deal. But he decided to experiment further with several agents.

A French scientist called Soubeiran had discovered chloroform in an impure state in 1831. At the same time Samuel Guthrie was working on it in the United States. But it was generally used in the treatment of asthma or hysteria, and not as an anaesthetic. This often happens; the real significance of discoveries and inventions is sometimes not recognised immediately.

Simpson experimented with chloroform and anaesthetised himself and his two assistants in the process. This has become the subject of many illustrations, such as Source 2. He then applied it mainly to women in childbirth (see Source 3).

Source 2

A nineteenth-century illustration showing the effect of chloroform on Simpson and his friends.

Source 3

Simpson's description of how he chloroformed a patient.

I placed her under the influence of the chloroform, by moistening, with half a teaspoon of the liquid, a pocket handkerchief, rolled up into a funnel shape, and with the broad or open end of the funnel placed over her mouth and nostrils. In consequence of the evaporation of the fluid it was once more renewed in about ten or twelve minutes. The child was expelled in about twenty-five minutes after the inhalation was begun.

Simpson thought that chloroform had three advantages over ether:

Source 4

James Simpson, *Account of a New Anaesthetic Agent as a Substitute for Sulphuric Ether in Surgery and Midwifery*, 1847.

1 A greatly less quantity of Chloroform...is requisite to produce the anaesthetic effect.
2 Its action is much more rapid and complete.
3 The inhalation and influence of chloroform...[are]...far more agreeable and pleasant than those of Ether.

requisite Necessary.

Remaining problems

Two major problems remained. One was that chloroform was more dangerous than earlier types of anaesthetic. It is just as well that the use of ether had provided some experience beforehand: otherwise there might have been many deaths from overdoses of chloroform.

The second problem was that there was much opposition to the use of chloroform. There were two main arguments as to why chloroform should not be used. One was based on religious grounds. The Bible showed that pain in childbirth was the result of Adam and Eve's expulsion from the Garden of Eden:

Source 5

Extract from Genesis (3:16).

In sorrow thou shalt bring forth children.

Against this, however, another part of Genesis could be quoted:

Source 6

Genesis (2.21).

And the Lord God caused a deep sleep to fall upon Adam and he slept; and He took one of his ribs, and closed up his flesh instead thereof.

But it was not until 1853, when Queen Victoria gave birth to Prince Leopold under anaesthetic, that anaesthetics became fully approved.

The other argument was based on medical grounds. Many surgeons considered that anaesthetics were dangerous – a strange argument, since the shock experienced by the fully conscious patient was a far greater one. The more skilled surgeons were soon won over by the prospect of being able to perform more complex operations.

How did anaesthetics affect the development of surgery?

One would think that the development of anaesthetics would have transformed surgery. What could the surgeon now not do? There would no longer be the need to complete an operation within a few minutes. Instead of merely amputating limbs, the surgeon could enter the abdominal and chest cavities. But for a time anaesthetics actually created more problems:

Source 7

G. T. Wrench, *Lord Lister: His Life and Work*, 1913.

This annihilation of the dreadful pain which made an operation such a gruesome thing in the past, and forbade any operations but those that were most urgent, opened out an apparently new area for surgery. But in hospitals the new blessing effected its own defeat. More operations were undertaken for lesser troubles, and the dread and terrible diseases of pyaemia and gangrene swept through the wards with redoubled fury.

annihilation Destruction.
effected Brought about.

The problem of pain had therefore not been solved. It was merely transferred from before to after the operation. Another breakthrough was therefore absolutely vital.

The development of antiseptics

As with anaesthetics, there was a long series of links in the development of antiseptics.

During the eighteenth century many surgeons came to the opinion that there was a connection between dirt and disease. There had also been research into microbes through the use of microscopes. But it was a long time before anyone put the two together. The usual belief was that infection was spread by foul air, or miasma. Then Louis Pasteur argued that the air is full of germs. Some surgeons therefore tried to exclude air from the wound by sealing it up with plaster immediately after the operation. This, of course, could actually hasten blood poisoning. Others tried stitching the wounds, leaving openings so that the pus could drain out. Others left the wound open, packing it with dressings which were changed every few days. There was great argument about these methods, and as to whether the water used should be boiling or cold. Other methods included alcohol soaks or iodine, bromide or creosote.

The contribution of Joseph Lister

Joseph Lister, Professor of Surgery at Edinburgh University, was especially influenced by Pasteur:

Source 8

From Lister's article in the *Lancet* (1867) 'On the antiseptic principle in the practice of surgery'.

> ...the essential cause of suppuration in wounds is decomposition, brought about by the influence of the atmosphere upon blood or serum....The septic property of the atmosphere depended, not on the oxygen or any gaseous constituent, but on minute organisms suspended in it....Upon this principle I have based a practice.

suppuration Pus.

He felt that the most important thing was to kill the bacteria in the air. The best way of doing this was by using a spray of carbolic acid. This had been used for many years to disinfect drains and cesspools. Lister sprayed the air in his operating theatres from 1871 onwards. This was partly a misunderstanding, since the bacteria were really on the operating instruments. Still, some of the spray landed on these and the risk of infection was therefore reduced.

Opposition

Lister encountered a great deal of opposition. This was partly because doctors and nurses complained about the smell of the carbolic spray or the amount of time taken to clean the operating area. Others felt that Lister was using new ideas for their own sake. Some doubted the theory on which Lister's ideas were based.

Part of the problem was that Lister did not communicate his theories very well in writing or in his speeches. He was always better known as a demonstrator. Hence those surgeons who worked with him were convinced. Those who had less direct contact with him were not.

Source 9

The use of carbolic spray before an operation.

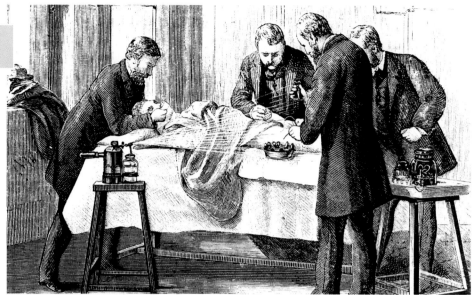

How important were antiseptics?

The use of antiseptics in surgery had a dramatic effect, greatly reducing the number of deaths from gangrene and blood poisoning.

Source 10

Figures provided by the Newcastle Infirmary to the *Lancet* in 1878 (adapted).

Death rate after operations in 1873 (before the introduction of antisepsis): 59.2%

Death rate after operations in 1878 (after the introduction of antisepsis): 4%

This success was encountered all over the country where antiseptics were tried.

On the other hand, antisepsis was often seen as a rather crude method of reducing infection. It could also burn and damage healthy tissue, as Alexander Fleming was later to point out (see Unit 13.3). Some surgeons preferred to follow the policy of cleanliness, usually associated with George Callender at St Bartholomew's Hospital. In fact, for some time cleanliness and antisepsis were rival approaches.

Eventually antisepsis and cleanliness came together to form the modern approach to surgery: asepsis. By the beginning of the twentieth century surgeons were operating in a germ-free environment. They wore gowns, masks and gloves and all their instruments were fully sterilised.

Questions

1 'No real progress could be made in surgery before the introduction of anaesthetics and antiseptics.' Why was this?

2 The introduction of anaesthetics came first. Did it quicken the growth of antiseptics?

3 'Their breakthroughs in medicine depended on the work of many other people.' Is this true in the case of (a) James Simpson and (b) Joseph Lister? Explain your answer.

Unit 11 · The revolution in nursing

The reputation of nursing in the early nineteenth century was very bad. Most nurses were untrained and were paid less than factory workers. They slept in the wards and part of their wages was paid in gin. By the second half of the century there had been a transformation in nursing which is often seen as a revolution. The person most commonly connected with the changes made to nursing in nineteenth-century hospitals was Florence Nightingale. This Unit explains her achievements and then considers them in broader perspective.

11.1 The career of Florence Nightingale

How did Florence Nightingale change nursing?

Florence Nightingale came from a middle-class family and her parents were horrified by her intention to go into nursing, especially when she served in the Middlesex Hospital during the 1854 cholera epidemic. But it was the Crimean War (1854–56) which made Florence Nightingale famous. Britain, France and Turkey were at war with Russia and the main campaigns were fought in the Crimean peninsula. A typical battle is shown in Source 1.

Source 1

The Battle of Alma (1854), which took place during the Crimean War when the British infantry stormed a Russian fortified position.

Around 100,000 British soldiers were killed or wounded. But many more fell ill through typhus and other diseases. The wounded and sick were treated at Scutari Hospital. The conditions there were dreadful and were described by one of the correspondents for *The Times*, William Russell:

Source 2

An extract from *The Times*, 14 October 1854.

No sufficient preparations have been made for the care of the wounded. Not only are there not sufficient surgeons, not only are there no dressers or male nurses, there is not even linen to make bandages.

The Secretary at War, Sir Sidney Herbert, knew Florence Nightingale and asked her to take control of the nursing of the troops at Scutari. The women she took with her were mostly members of religious orders. The doctors at Scutari were at first strongly opposed to any interference from women nurses. But Florence Nightingale persisted. She immediately brought about enormous changes. All the wards were scrubbed clean after the accumulated filth was removed in wheelbarrows. The windows were opened and fresh air allowed to circulate through the wards. When she arrived she found no facilities, no plumbing, no kitchens, even. All these were set up, along with recreation rooms to assist convalescence. Through persistence and continuous care she reduced the death rate among the soldiers in Scutari hospital from 42 per cent to 2 per cent.

Source 3

The wounded in a hospital in the Crimea before Florence Nightingale's arrival.

Source 4

A hospital ward in Scutari after the changes introduced by Florence Nightingale.

Individuals in history sometimes have legends built up around them, which become the main reason for their later fame. Florence Nightingale became known as the 'Lady with the Lamp' (see Sources 5 to 7):

Source 5

An extract from Russell's despatches from the Crimea.

When all the medical officers have retired for the night and silence and darkness have settled…upon those miles of prostrate sick, she may be observed alone with a little lamp in her hand making her solitary rounds.

Source 6

An illustration in the *London Evening News*, February 1855.

THE NIGHTINGALE'S SONG TO THE SICK
SOLDIER.

LISTEN, soldier, to the tale of the tender NIGHTINGALE,
 'Tis a charm that soon will ease your wounds so cruel,
Singing medicine for your pain, in a sympathising strain,
 With a jug, jug, jug of lemonade or gruel.

Singing bandages and lint; salve and cerate without stint,
 Singing plenty both of liniment and lotion,
And your mixtures pushed about, and the pills for you served out,
 With alacrity and promptitude of motion.

Singing light and gentle hands, and a nurse who understands
 How to manage every sort of application,
From a poultice to a leech; whom you haven't got to teach
 The way to make a poppy fomentation.

Singing pillow for you smoothed, smart and ache and anguish soothed,
 By the readiness of feminine invention;
Singing fever's thirst allayed, and the bed you've tumbled, made,
 With a careful and considerate attention.

Singing succour to the brave, and a rescue from the grave,
 Hear the NIGHTINGALE that's come to the Crimea,
'Tis a NIGHTINGALE as strong in her heart as in her song,
 To carry out so gallant an idea.

Source 7

'The Nightingale's Song',
Punch, 1855.

In fact, most of her best work was still to come. After reorganising the hospital at Scutari, Florence Nightingale was appointed General Superintendent of the Female Nursing Establishment of the Army. She spent much of her time preparing reports. She put her ideas in her *Notes on Hospitals* and *Notes on Nursing*, both of which were published after the war in 1859.

Questions

1 a What are the main differences between the scenes shown in Sources 3 and 4?

b What was Florence Nightingale hoping to achieve by making these changes?

2 What do Sources 5 and 6 show of Florence Nightingale's qualities as a nurse?

3 What does Source 7 show of nursing in the 1850s?

4 Why do you think Florence Nightingale is better remembered as the Lady with the Lamp than as the lady who reorganised nursing?

11.2   The impact of Florence Nightingale

What was the influence of Florence Nightingale's reforms?

British nursing and hospital administration were affected in a variety of ways by Florence Nightingale's reforms.

The training of hospital nurses

On her return to England from the Crimean War, she raised around £50,000 which was used to set up the Nightingale School of Nursing at St Thomas's Hospital in 1860. This was to influence the training of nurses throughout the country. Every major hospital proceeded to set up a training school and to use her ideas.

She emphasised a number of points that every nurse should follow. Nursing required total dedication and a complete understanding of medical procedures. This was very important if the nurse was to be a skilled assistant to the doctor. A certain amount of all-round and medical training was therefore essential. This was provided by the matron of St Thomas's Hospital, Mrs Wardroper.

Source 1

Probationers outside St Thomas's Hospital. Mrs Wardroper is on the right.

Miss Nightingale continued to serve as an adviser and organiser. She checked the training in her school and approved the appointment of nurses from it. Most important were the matrons who came through the school, as they spread her methods in other hospitals throughout the country.

The popularity of nursing

The professionalisation of nursing made it much easier for women to take up a career in nursing. The appeal was very widespread, and many girls were attracted. Nursing offered a prospect for adventurous girls to escape from the social constraints of Victorian England.

Source 2

The number of nurses, according to the population census.

1861	24,821
1901	61,159

The improvement in record-keeping

One of the essential functions of any hospital is to keep detailed records on all patients. Modern methods began with Florence Nightingale, who organised records of admissions, discharges, types of illness, treatment and deaths.

The design of hospitals

Florence Nightingale had definite ideas about the planning of hospitals and their equipment. She attached great importance to fresh air and sunlight for the patients. Plenty of space and a design which made for easy cleaning were also priorities. Her main influence was the pavilion style which included both of these features (see Source 3).

Source 3

The new St Thomas's Hospital. This was built in accordance with Florence Nightingale's instructions.

The effect abroad

Florence Nightingale's *Notes on Nursing* were used all over the world, and almost every country in Europe introduced her ideas on training and hospital care. She also influenced the founder of the Red Cross, Henri Dunant. When he visited London in 1872, he said:

Source 4

An extract from a talk given by Henri Dunant in London in 1872.

Though I am known as the founder of the Red Cross and the originator of the Convention of Geneva, it is to an Englishwoman that all the honour of that Convention is due. What inspired me…was the work of Miss Florence Nightingale in the Crimea.

How important was Florence Nightingale?

Was Dunant exaggerating the importance of Florence Nightingale? As with any famous historical figure, we need to achieve an overall perspective on her influence.

Nightingale as an originator

As we have already seen, her positive achievements were enormous. There is general agreement among historians about her contributions to nursing:

Source 5

Charles E. Rosenberg, *Explaining Epidemics and Other Studies in the History of Medicine*, 1992.

[She was] one of the few individuals who exerted a peculiar and indispensable influence on that history....Her two most widely read books, *Notes on Nursing* and *Notes on Hospitals*, had an extraordinary success in the second half of the century; it would be hard to overestimate her influence in the shaping of modern nursing and the reordering of hospitals.

Her personal influence was of vital importance. Quite simply, she had a strong character and got things done.

Source 6

A photograph of Florence Nightingale in later life.

Source 7

Philip Rhodes, *An Outline History of Medicine*, 1985.

She was an autocratic woman of iron will and imposed her ideas of nursing and medical care on those in authority and on her nurses. She had friends in the high place of the Cabinet. Through an endless stream of correspondence and personal overwhelming contacts she determined to improve nursing education and care whenever and wherever she could.

Nightingale's reforms as part of a process

The nursing reforms of Florence Nightingale did not emerge in a vacuum. Important though they were, they were part of a process.

As we have seen in Unit 4, there had already been a general move towards improvements in hospital care during the eighteenth century. Further changes were also taking place in the nineteenth century, both in Britain and on the Continent.

In Britain, several nursing orders were set up between 1800 and 1850. These included the Sisters of Mercy and the Irish Sisters of Charity. There were also several other orders organised by the Church of England. On the Continent, Pastor Theodore Fliedner set up the Deaconess Institute at Kaiserswerth in Germany, at which deaconesses were given training to care for the sick. By 1864 there were thirty-four similar establishments throughout Germany. Elizabeth Fry visited Kaiserswerth and set up the Institute of Nursing Sisters in Britain. She considered it necessary…

Source 8

The view of Elizabeth Fry.

…for a class of women to attend the sick altogether different from the hireling nurses.

This directly anticipated Nightingale's views and policies.

Another development was very important for the nursing revolution. The nineteenth century was a period in which many hospitals were built. Some were run and paid for by voluntary organisations. Cottage hospitals were also opened; by 1900 the number had increased to 300. Their purpose was to offer many of the services of a large infirmary but on a miniature scale. They were particularly useful for rural areas. The expansion of voluntary and cottage hospitals meant an ever growing demand for Nightingale nurses.

Limitations of Nightingals's reforms

There were also areas in which the Nightingale revolution had scarcely entered and where work was done by other people to fill the gap. The first example was nursing with the poor, which had hardly been affected by the Nightingale changes in nursing. An attempt was therefore made in one or two areas, such as the Brownlow Hill Workhouse in Liverpool, to open up the wards and to improve conditions. Increasingly the central government took on the responsibility of encouraging local authorities to provide hospital care for the poor. After 1867, for example, the Poor Law Unions (established earlier, in 1834) were ordered to set up infirmaries. The major cities, especially London, Birmingham and Liverpool, built a series of new hospitals for the poor and also separate fever hospitals for infectious diseases. By 1900 these had become the most numerous of all the hospitals.

There was a second development which was carried out by other people. This was the growth of nursing outside hospitals, especially district nursing. This had been started by a doctor from Liverpool, William Rathbone, to serve his city. He seized the initiative in 1861 and set up at the Liverpool Royal Infirmary a training school which would produce nurses to work among the poor in their homes. He co-operated closely with Florence Nightingale and used many of her ideas. By 1887 district nurses were serving most cities in Britain and were also spreading quickly in the rural areas.

Third, nursing on the battlefield was by no means confined to Nightingale nurses. Henri Dunant was too modest in giving to Florence Nightingale all the credit for the founding of the Red Cross (see Source 4). In fact he had seen the terrible slaughter on the battlefield at Solferino in 1860 during the war for the unification of Italy. He was so horrified that he set up the International Red Cross in 1864. This extended Nightingale's changes into an area they had not yet entered – the international field.

Shortcomings of Nightingale's ideas and changes

There were, finally, shortcomings in Florence Nightingale's ideas and changes. Her ideas on medicine were backward-looking. She was a believer in the miasma theory of disease and did not accept the idea of the contagionists – that a specific disease was caused by a specific germ. This is why she placed so much importance on the cleanliness of the hospital ward. Stale air could breed anything, she thought:

Source 9

Florence Nightingale, *Notes on Nursing*, 1859.

It is quite ripe to breed smallpox, scarlet fever, diphtheria, or anything else you please.

The contagionist approach she considered to be merely an excuse for inaction...

Source 10

Florence Nightingale, *Notes on Nursing*, 1859.

...affording to certain classes of minds, chiefly in the Southern and less educated parts of Europe a satisfactory reason for pestilence, and an adequate excuse for non-exertion to prevent its recurrence.

Florence Nightingale was more expert at organisation than in medical theories. But even here she missed out on one very important possibility. She did not consider that official government recognition of the qualifications of her nurses was necessary. This was out of line with the rest of the medical profession, where government-approved qualifications came to apply to doctors and midwives. It was also out of step with a number of other countries, where state registration was introduced – in New Zealand, Canada, Australia, Austria-Hungary, Belgium, Germany and even Cuba. It was not introduced into Britain until the Nurses Registration Act of 1919. This is possibly an indication that Florence Nightingale had become so self-confident that she distrusted even the role of the government in preserving what she had accomplished.

Questions

1 How much were the changes in nursing due to Florence Nightingale, and how much to other factors?

2 What did Florence Nightingale not achieve in nursing?

3 Look at Sources 9 and 10. How do they show that Florence Nightingale was a miasmatist? Did this matter? (Use any other sources in this Unit to support your view.)

Unit 12 · Medical training and women

At the beginning of the nineteenth century three-quarters of all people who practised medicine were untrained. By 1900 great improvements had been made to the training and qualification of doctors. Why and how did this happen? And how effective were the improvements?

Why and how was medical training improved?

Why?

There were three main reasons for the improvement. First, more people were becoming wealthy, as a result of industry and commerce. One of the things on which they were willing to spend their money was a higher standard of medical care. This meant that there was a growing demand for doctors and nurses of the highest quality.

Second, improved training was essential if the people practising medicine were to keep up with the rapid advances being made in germ theory, anaesthetics and antiseptics. And third, the government was becoming increasingly aware that it had a responsibility for the standard of medical care, just as it realised that it needed to do something about the state of public health (see Unit 9).

How?

At the beginning of the century there was much rivalry between the various branches of the profession – the physicians, surgeons and apothecaries. Each had its own system of membership and qualifications. Physicians had degrees and acted as hospital consultants or as private doctors to the wealthy. Apothecaries usually acted as general practitioners, and there was an examination for membership of the Society of Apothecaries from 1815. Surgeons were regulated by a diploma issued by the Royal College of Surgeons from 1800.

But such qualifications were not recognised in all parts of the country. The physicians conducted their examinations orally in Latin. These tested knowledge of Greek and Latin medical texts rather than of more recent medical developments. Even more curiously, only students from Oxford and Cambridge could take the examination.

By the middle of the century the government was becoming more involved in providing standard qualifications. In 1858 the Medical Act made sure that all medical graduates received the same qualification so that they could practise in any part of the country. A General Medical Council (GMC) was set up to supervise the qualifications and to keep a list of approved doctors. This was called the General Register. The GMC also laid down what the medical student should know before being permitted to qualify as a doctor. Examination questions now had to be set on anatomy, physiology, pharmacy, surgery and midwifery.

How effective were these improvements?

There are two ways of looking at this. On the one hand, historians have argued that physicians and trainee doctors had a much greater sense of responsibility to society. The general practitioner, too, had a much improved reputation for caring for his patients. These points are shown in Sources 1, 2 and 3.

Source 1

Philip Rhodes, *An Outline History of Medicine*, 1985.

These early and subsequent efforts to control, improve and enhance the educational standards of the medical profession have undoubtedly had a beneficial effect in the service of patients.

More important perhaps is the underlying idea that the profession as a whole owes a duty to the public as a whole and that the doctors must demonstrate to the public that they are discharging those duties satisfactorily.

Source 2

M. Jeanne Peterson, *The Medical Profession in Mid-Victorian London*, 1978.

Steeplechases in the dissecting room, cheating on the Latin examination, flirting with the barmaid, gin-and-water until three o'clock in the morning, these were the stereotypical activities of the medical student of the 1840's. By the 1880's the press presented a new image of the medical student: surrounded by books, a model of a human skull at his elbow, he laboured over his studies with gravity and decorum late into the night....The new image was the product of discipline – not only the self-discipline of study but also the command of the profession over those it was training for admission to its ranks.

Source 3

A painting by Luke Fildes (1891), showing a general practitioner caring for a sick child.

The GP was also willing to extend the range of his visits. This, in turn, was helped by improvements in transport (see Source 4).

Source 4

A general practitioner on his rounds in Burnley in 1900.

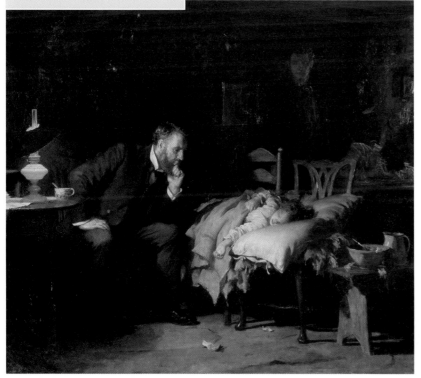

On the other hand, there is a more negative view of how changes in training affected the population. There were still huge social differences in Victorian England. Many people, especially those living in slums, never got to see a doctor at all. All visits to – or by – a doctor still had to be paid for. There were some attempts to reduce the payments by setting up sick clubs for poorer people. But it was not until the coming of the welfare state in the twentieth century that the real breakthrough occurred here.

Also, the level of training was still very general. There were alarming gaps in knowledge about the details of anatomy and drugs. Once they were in practice, many GPs did not bother with a preliminary examination of their patient; they ignored both pulse and temperature, and they rarely used the stethoscope.

Questions

1 In what different ways do Sources 1, 2 and 3 examine the theme of 'responsibility' in medicine?

2 Draw up a balanced argument about the improvements in any remaining problems of training in the nineteenth century.

12.2 Developments in midwifery and obstetrics

Source 1

A major trend in the eighteenth century had been the replacement of some female midwives by men. For some, this caused a crisis of identity.

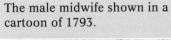
The male midwife shown in a cartoon of 1793.

Source 2

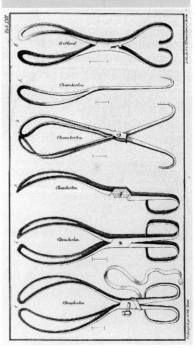
Forceps in use in the mid-nineteenth century.

In some ways this proved an advantage. It ended the old prejudices against men examining women. Getting rid of such barriers was essential if medicine was to make any real progress. It also meant that midwifery came more into contact with the hospitals and with specialists. This made it possible to use more advanced techniques in obstetrics and new forceps (see Source 2).

Placing midwifery more firmly in the hospitals also meant that anaesthetics could be used – once Queen Victoria had given her approval.

In other ways, the entry of men into midwifery proved to be a disadvantage. It meant that women were given the routine jobs or merely acted as assistants to male obstetricians. Female midwives were used for the poorer part of the population. The Obstetrical Society believed that poor women were stronger and less sensitive than richer women and that they could therefore be treated outside hospital. These developments may also have slowed the advance of the recognition of women doctors, since it was assumed that women in medicine could still be occupied by midwifery outside hospitals – or by nursing inside.

Questions

1 Explain the meaning of Source 1. How effective is it as a comment on male midwives?

2 Describe the main difference between the forceps shown in Source 2 here and those in Source 4 on page 29. What evidence can you see of (a) continuity and (b) progress?

12.3 The qualification of women as doctors

What prevented women from being doctors?

There had been women physicians in the Ancient World but not in the Middle Ages. During the reign of Henry V an Act of Parliament had been passed preventing women from practising medicine. Women were also unable to become members of medical guilds. The nineteenth century imposed further obstacles. The 1858 Medical Act stated that only candidates passing the appropriate examinations could qualify as doctors. Since no university admitted women, this closed yet another door.

For much of the Victorian period there was strong opposition to the very idea of women setting up as doctors. The arguments can be set out under three headings:

1. Social Women as doctors would upset the male control over the professions and would set all sorts of undesirable examples.

2. Psychological It was assumed that women would make medicine more trivial. Much the same argument was used against giving women the vote.

3. Biological Women would be acting against the normal inclinations of their sex.

These reasons provide a typical view of the prejudices in English society. Similar attitudes existed in the law and politics.

What was the importance of Elizabeth Garrett?

Her career

A breakthrough was made by Elizabeth Blackwell, who qualified as a doctor in the United States. Elizabeth Garrett (1836–1917), who met her in London in 1859, was determined to follow her example.

She gained an apprenticeship after working for three years with Dr Joshua Plaskitt in London. She felt that this entitled her to a university place. But she was rejected by St Andrews and Edinburgh because she was a woman. Instead, she was taught privately by Dr Alexander Keiller of Edinburgh University and in gynaecology and midwifery by Dr David Murray.

In 1865 she was given the opportunity of taking an examination at the Society of Apothecaries. She easily passed the oral questions they put to her. She was now entitled to the degree of LSA (Licentiate of the Society of Apothecaries). She was, however, determined to gain an MD. This she obtained in Paris in 1869 with the highest possible grade. After her marriage to Dr James Anderson she was known as Elizabeth Garrett Anderson. She pursued her career vigorously, becoming a lecturer in the London School of Medicine for Women. In 1883 she was made Dean.

Her influence

Elizabeth Garrett is usually seen as the most important single influence enabling women to qualify as doctors. She had a clear vision of what she wanted to achieve. She showed enormous strength of character in persevering when obstacles were put up against her. She was also logical in her answers to those who argued that what she proposed to do was disgusting.

On the other hand, her achievement needs to be placed in perspective, like that of Florence Nightingale. She did not bring about the changes by herself. There were other women who were also trying to gain admission to British universities. When they failed, they too gained MDs abroad, usually at Zurich in Switzerland. They included Frances Elizabeth Hoggan in 1870, Elizabeth Walker in 1872, and Louisa Atkins.

More influential than these was Sophia Jex-Blake, whose main ambition was to found a medical school for women in Britain. Both Elizabeth Garrett and Elizabeth Blackwell had to be persuaded to support this scheme. Sophia Jex-Blake found the site and building at 30 Henrietta Street and the School officially opened in 1874. By the following year there were twenty-three students. It then sought recognition for its degrees from one of the universities. After much delay it eventually secured the support of the King's and Queen's College of Physicians, now the Irish College. From that time onwards enrolments climbed steadily.

There were also other influences – which had nothing to do with the campaign by women. The most important of these was the shortage of doctors in Victorian Britain. To some extent this was brought about by raising the standard of training and qualifications. Many were now asking whether the country could afford to exclude women. Finally, some politicians felt that there was a moral case for allowing women to qualify. During the 1870s there were many debates in Parliament, in which MPs were prepared to argue the case for women's rights in medicine. Eventually, in 1876, Parliament passed an Act to remove restrictions on granting medical qualifications 'on the grounds of sex'.

Questions

Study Sources A to H and answer the questions which follow.

Source A

A *Punch* cartoon in 1865 showing the expected effect of women doctors.

LADY-PHYSICIANS.

WHO IS THIS INTERESTING INVALID? IT IS YOUNG REGINALD DE BRACES, WHO HAS SUCCEEDED IN CATCHING A BAD COLD, IN ORDER THAT HE MIGHT SEND FOR THAT RISING PRACTITIONER, DR. ARABELLA BOLUS!

Source B

From a newspaper column in 1859 on Elizabeth Blackwell's visit to Britain.

It is impossible that Dr Blackwell, whose hands reek with gore, can be possessed of the same nature or feelings as the generality of women.

Source C

A letter from Elizabeth Garrett to her father, 18 June 1862.

...legal recognition must be given here in England. I think my work is...plain, viz. to go on acting as pioneer towards this end, even though by doing so I spend the best years of my life in sowing that of which other students will reap the benefit.

Source D

The number of doctors in the population, according to the population census.

	Total population	No. of doctors
1841	16,000,000	15,800
1871	23,000,000	14,600

Source E

A contemporary illustration showing Elizabeth Garrett qualifying in Paris in 1870.

Source F

Enrolments at the London School of Medicine for Women.

1875	23
1887	77
1889	91
1892	133
1896	159
1903	318
1917	441

Source G

Arthur Roebuck, a Liberal MP, speaking in the House of Commons, 3 March 1875.

You may talk for a month; you may bring great law to bear upon this question; you may quote names great in history, arts and science. But you cannot rub out the stain which will be on this House if it refuses to do justice for women...and prevents them from using their intellect...in a fair, honest, and upright manner for their own good.

Source H

An extract from the medical journal the *Lancet*, 1876.

If those women who are seeking, at an extravagant cost of time and money, to enter the medical profession, were content to work in the only department of medical practice which is open to them – namely as midwives and nurses – no objections could be fairly raised, provided they always practised under the supervision of qualified medical practitioners....But...the female medical students in London ...are striving to be placed upon the Medical Register and then to please themselves what branches of medicine they shall engage in.

1. What do Sources A and B show of the objections of some men to the qualification of women as doctors?

2. Do Sources E and F show that the aim expressed in Source C succeeded?

3. How might Source E be seen at the time by (a) male doctors in Britain and (b) women trying to qualify as doctors?

4. How do Sources B and G disagree?

5. Use Sources C, D and G to explain why women were eventually allowed to become doctors.

6. What other types of source would be useful to show how women were allowed to become doctors?

Transferring vital data on
patients from one
hospital to another.

This photograph shows the transfer of medical data from one hospital
to another. It is an example of the advanced technology which has
become increasingly common since 1900. It also symbolises a further
breakthrough in medicine and public health, which is the theme of Part
3 of this book. There have been new problems, and the solutions have
not always been forthcoming. But the pace of change has rapidly
accelerated. Unit 13 looks at the reduction of some diseases and the
growth of others. It also covers improvements in surgery and technology
and the use of new drugs, especially penicillin. Unit 14 examines the
growing role played in medicine and health by the state, especially
since 1945. There have also been changes in the way women relate to
medicine, which are shown in Unit 15. Finally, alternative medicine
continues to exist (Unit 16), although it, too, has experienced some new
developments.

Unit 13 · Disease, technology and drugs

13.1 Disease and illness

We saw in Unit 6 that different diseases behaved in different ways between 1450 and 1750 and in the period 1750–1900. How have diseases behaved in the twentieth century? And has there been an overall trend in their behaviour?

Has there been an overall trend?

One disease has disappeared

Vaccination is one of the great success stories of modern medicine. As the result of a worldwide programme of vaccination, smallpox has been wiped out throughout the world. Vaccination is no longer carried out in Britain.

Some diseases have been greatly reduced

One of these is tuberculosis. Both consumption and scrofula were very widespread in the nineteenth and early twentieth centuries – both associated with poverty. Living conditions have, however, generally improved as a result of the welfare state. Although there are still several million people in Britain below the poverty line, very few live in the worst conditions experienced in the nineteenth century. Milk supplies have been purified by the process of pasteurisation. Anyone who does get tuberculosis now stands a better chance of being cured by an antibiotic called streptomycin. Tuberculosis is therefore a disease which now affects the Third World rather than Britain or Europe.

Another disease which has been significantly reduced is poliomyelitis (polio). Usually caught in childhood, this causes paralysis in various parts of the body. A vaccine was introduced by Jonas Edward Salk in 1953 and this is now widely used. There is a chance that polio will eventually go the same way as smallpox. Cholera and typhoid have also become rare in Britain – because of the improvements in water supplies. They do, however, occur from time to time in Third World countries where water becomes infected.

So-called childhood diseases have become a thing of the past. It was once thought that children should be allowed contact with chicken-pox, mumps or measles so that they did not catch them as adults when the effect might be more serious. The same was once thought about smallpox too (see page 42). Since the 1950s, however, inoculations have been developed against all of these ailments, together with whooping cough and rubella (German measles).

Some diseases have increased in importance

One of these is influenza (or flu), which exists in many different forms and which strikes the elderly most severely. The worst epidemic in history occurred at the end of the First World War. In Britain, 750,000 caught the disease, of whom 151,446 died. Although there has never again been an outbreak as serious as this, various forms reappear frequently.

Heart disease and cancer have also claimed more victims. These are sometimes seen as the diseases of advanced civilisations. They are aggravated by unhealthy diet and stress, and by smoking and heavy drinking. But it has also been argued that heart disease and cancer are now more widespread only because so many other killer diseases have been reduced.

Source 1

A ward for AIDS patients.

Some new diseases have appeared

Strictly speaking, some problems have only recently been recognised as illnesses. One of these is occupational illness either caused or encouraged by a person's work. But other diseases are transmitted by infection. By far the most deadly of these is AIDS (Acquired Immune Deficiency Syndrome), which was first identified in 1973. This is caused by the Human Immunodeficiency Virus (HIV), which is passed by unprotected sexual intercourse with an infected partner or by direct blood contact through, for example, sharing needles between drug misusers. HIV breaks down the body's ability to resist infection so that patients in the stage known as full-blown AIDS fall victim to a range of diseases or cancers. Despite worldwide research, no cure had been found by the mid-1990s.

Questions

1 Copy out and fill in the following table, using Units 6 and 13.

	Column 1 1450–1750	Column 2 Since 1900
Diseases in decline		
Diseases which disappeared		
Diseases on the increase		
New diseases		

2 What conclusions do you draw from this table?

3 What changes and events in the nineteenth century influenced your entries in column 2 of the table?

4 Unit 6 dealt with the bubonic plague. Some people have seen AIDS as the 'new plague'. Is this, in your view, an accurate description?

13.2 Developments in medical technology and surgery

The twentieth century has seen a huge number of changes in these areas. We can do no more than examine a few examples of each.

Medical technology

The first major breakthrough came with the development of X-rays. These have two main purposes. One is diagnostic – to examine parts of the body which cannot normally be seen. The other is therapeutic – to destroy cancerous growths without damaging healthy tissue.

There was a strong element of chance in the discovery of X-rays. Professor Wilhelm von Röntgen was examining the effects of cathode rays in 1895 when he noticed that a piece of barium-coated paper near the tube he was using had developed a luminous glow. Instead of simply moving the paper out of his way, he placed his hand between the tube and the paper and saw the outline of the bones. He then converted the pictures to photographic plates. He published his findings in various medical journals, including the *Lancet*. Röntgen's discovery was soon used in hospitals to detect broken bones or the exact position in the body of foreign objects like bullets. This was accelerated by the First World War, after which many hospitals set up an X-ray unit. These were also able to detect problems in the stomach or the lungs, thanks to the work of Walter B. Cannon before 1900 in applying X-rays to the gastro-intestinal tract. It is now possible to scan the entire body.

Source 1

A patient having a brain scan.

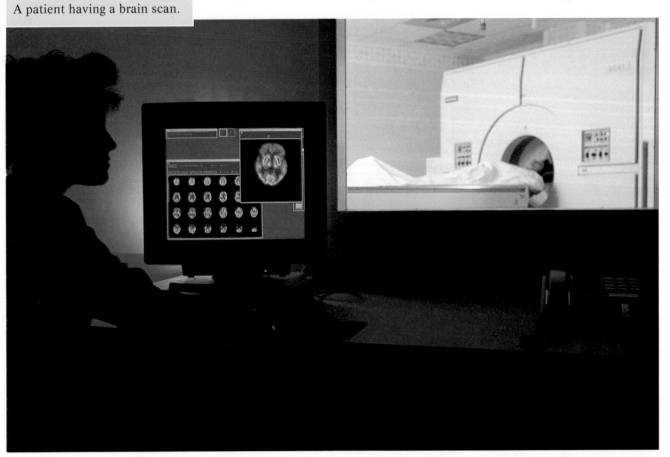

Source 2

A machine providing support for a patient with kidney problems. This purifies the blood, a process normally carried out by the kidneys, by a method known as dialysis.

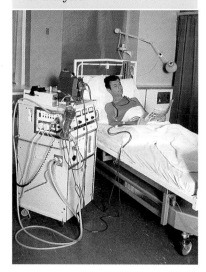

The work on the therapeutic effects of X-rays was carried out in France by Pierre and Marie Curie. Marie Curie was a physicist, not a doctor. She discovered radium, which she extracted from uranium ore after years of incredibly hard work. She quickly saw the possibilities that radium had in the treatment of cancer. The idea was to destroy some cells while leaving others intact. This has become a key method in treating certain forms of cancer.

Sources 1–4 are some other examples of how twentieth-century technology has transformed patient care in hospitals.

Source 3

A heart and lung machine. In particularly acute cases it is sometimes difficult for the patient to breath unaided. There may also have been heart failure. The heart and lungs are kept working in order to keep the patient alive.

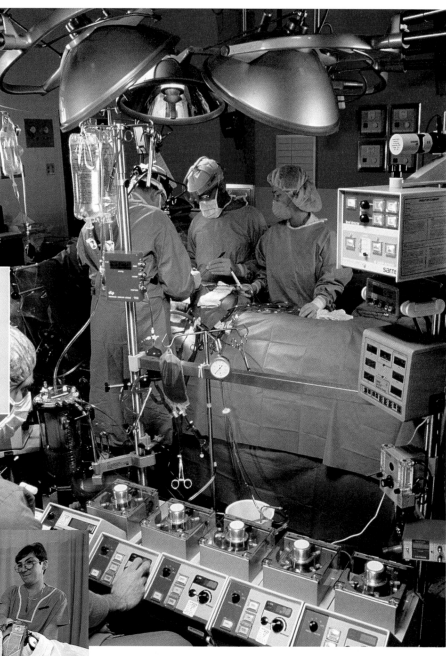

Source 4

A foetal monitoring machine. The purpose is to ensure that the foetus is developing normally and to check its position before birth.

Blood transfusions

The problem of blood shortage had baffled surgeons for centuries. During the seventeenth century attempts had been made to transfer blood from animals to people and from one person to another. Rubber or glass tubes were used but such operations were always unsuccessful. In times of war many battle casualties died from loss of blood, and during the late nineteenth and early twentieth centuries there was a new urgency to find a way of preventing this.

The breakthrough came as a result of three major developments, which now made blood transfusions possible. The **first** was the invention of the hollow needle, to induce blood directly and cleanly into the patient's artery. The **second** was the discovery and description of blood groups by Landsteiner in 1901. This meant that the blood of the recipient could be matched carefully to that of the donor to reduce the chance of the new blood being 'rejected'. The **third** was the storage of blood for when it was needed. This was made possible by the introduction of a method of preventing the blood from coagulating; this was largely the result of the work of Albert Hustin, who added glucose and sodium citrate to blood and reported his methods in 1914.

All this took some time and it was the First World War (1914–18) which speeded the whole process up. Hundreds of thousands of wounded soldiers proved the strongest possible reason for getting the new methods into operation. Blood treated with glucose and sodium citrate was used on the battlefields from 1917 and was soon collected and stored in blood banks for extensive use. The Second World War (1939–45) added a similar sense of urgency and the National Blood Transfusion Service was set up in Britain during this period. These are typical examples of war acting as a catalyst for medical change. Blood transfusions were to be of vital importance for the development of modern surgery. Without them, most modern heart or transplant operations would have been out of the question.

Source 5

A team of doctors and nurses to care for serious heart cases.

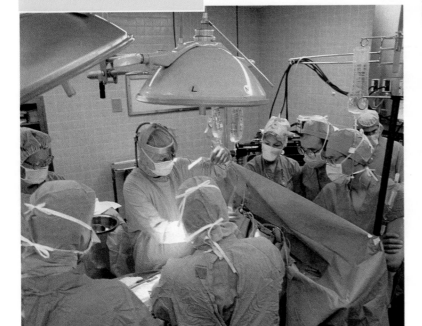

Surgery

Surgery has become much more complex, with surgeons specialising in particular branches such as heart or brain surgery. Each surgeon is backed up by teams of nurses and specialists and by equipment (see Source 5).

There is now an extremely low rate of infection. The emphasis has moved away from antisepsis to asepsis; carbolic sprays are no longer used. Antibiotics control whatever infection follows an operation.

There have also been advances in anaesthetics. There is now a fine balance between keeping the patient unconscious and giving too much anaesthetic. This is the purpose of the equipment shown in Source 6.

Source 6

Anaesthesiological machinery in 1950.

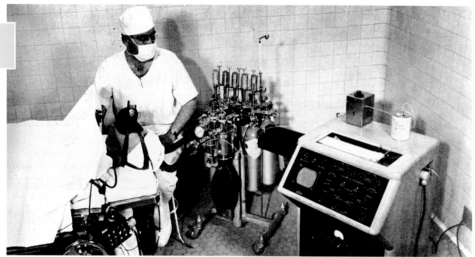

The two most recent developments are spare-part and key-hole surgery. The first has made it possible to transplant organs like the heart, liver, kidney or lung. The other reduces the size of incisions by inserting tubes containing surgical instruments and monitoring devices. Increasingly, surgery will be done by remote control with the assistance of a computer.

Questions

1 Using the evidence in Sources 1 to 6 write an account of what machinery is available in a modern hospital. Compare this with hospitals in the nineteenth century.

2 Twentieth-century surgery has moved from antisepsis to asepsis. Does this mean that there was no point to the nineteenth-century developments in antisepsis?

13.3 Penicillin

The development of antibiotics has been vital for the treatment of infections. The earliest and most important was penicillin.

Why and how was penicillin discovered?

The discovery of penicillin was the result of a complex set of factors which were seen separately, but which influenced one another.

During the 1870s and 1880s the *Lancet* published many papers on the healing properties of fungi. But all over the world mould had been used for centuries as a means of quickening the healing of wounds – by peoples as far apart as the Mayas of Central America, the Indians of Brazil and the Zulus of southern Africa. Why, therefore, was there a sudden interest?

Part of the reason is that the study of bacteria had become more and more widespread during the nineteenth century (see Unit 8). Research was being carried out all the time into different types of bacteria. Meanwhile, quite separately from all this, Charles Darwin had developed the theory that various species had evolved through struggle and of the 'survival of the fittest'. Some medical scientists saw possibilities here. Might not some microbes fight and overcome others? Paul Vuillemin certainly thought so, and called the process *antibiosis*. This is the origin of the word *antibiotics*.

The search for a 'magic bullet'

At this stage no one quite knew how to use the idea of antibiosis. Instead, much attention was given to antiseptics to kill all bacteria. But there was an important change. Lister (see pages 64–5) had used antiseptic spray externally – in the air and on wounds. Now the German chemist Paul Ehrlich tried, through experiments, to find a 'magic bullet', an antiseptic which could be taken internally to destroy a disease. He tried and failed 605 times before producing Salvarsan. But this was effective only in the treatment of syphilis.

Ehrlich inspired other researchers to try to find a drug which could be taken internally to destroy harmful bacteria of all kinds. Almroth Wright, especially, worked on this idea of 'generalised immunisation' at St Mary's Hospital, Paddington. One of his assistants was Alexander Fleming.

The effect of the First World War

The need for such a drug was made more urgent when Britain was plunged into the First World War. Fleming saw the treatment of wounded soldiers in Boulogne and was convinced that antiseptics were not the answer. In fact, he argued, they often did much harm by destroying healthy tissue as well as infected areas:

Source 1

W. Howard Hughes, *Alexander Fleming and Penicillin*, 1974.

'I remember', Fleming said, 'that I used to be told to be most careful to use antiseptics in the dressing of wounds – carbolic acid, boric acid, peroxide of hydrogen. I could see for myself that these antiseptics did not kill all the microbes, but was told they killed some, and that the results were better than if no antiseptics had been used at all. At that time I was in no position to argue.'

Fleming and many others were convinced that a drug was needed to replace antiseptics altogether. Ehrlich's 'magic bullet' was the right idea, but the wrong approach.

The accidental discovery

The search was on throughout the 1920s. In 1922 Fleming discovered the enzyme *lysozyme*, but this did not lead to a new drug. Then, in 1928 he returned from a holiday to find that a prepared culture he had left on a dish had been attacked by a mould. Fleming conducted an investigation and, in a paper he published in 1928, he identified the mould as *penicillium*.

Unfortunately, he was never able to reproduce the same experiment. So where did the fungus come from? Three theories have been suggested. One is that the spores came through the door, another that they blew in through the window, the third that they entered through the ventilation system. It was therefore a discovery rather than an invention.

Source 2

A photograph of Alexander Fleming working in his laboratory, 1951.

Why and how was penicillin developed?

'M & B'

For a while, nothing further happened. Fleming was unable to repeat the reaction and made no further discoveries. In the meantime, in the 1930s a new drug, which was neither an antibiotic nor an antiseptic, was developed in Germany. Called Protonsil, this was based on a wool dye and was the first of a class of drug known as the sulphonamides. Its inventor was Gerhard Domagk and it was produced commercially in 1938 by May and Baker. It soon became known as M & B.

Rather as in the case of Ehrlich's 'magic bullet', this again stimulated the search for an antibiotic – but by people other than Fleming. From 1938 a research team at Oxford University continued to work on penicillin. It was soon established that the penicillin affected many forms of bacteria but not the tissue or the normal defences of the white cells. Led by Howard Florey and Ernst Chain, the team tried to refine penicillin and make it a usable drug. The problem was that it was needed in large quantities to guarantee success. But it was difficult to make and only very small quantities were available.

The Second World War and mass production

How could penicillin be mass produced? The Second World War was a vital factor. It transformed the supply of penicillin. In 1943 there were stocks to treat only 100 patients. By 1944 production had reached 3,000 billion units per month, enough for all Allied casualties in France and Italy. This was a real breakthrough. When the war ended in 1945 the pharmaceutical companies were able to gear this mass production for the public at large.

Other antibiotics

Penicillin is still the most widely used antibiotic, but it is not the only one. Others soon followed. They had certain advantages over penicillin. First, they could deal more effectively with specific types of illnesses and infections. Streptomycin, for example, was discovered in 1944, and proved better for the treatment of tuberculosis. Second, many people are allergic to penicillin – that is to say, they suffer side effects. These are less common with more recent antibiotics like Tetracyclin (discovered in 1953) and Mitomycin (1956).

Who developed penicillin?

Ask anyone who developed penicillin and the answer will almost certainly be 'Alexander Fleming'. Try it! This is because of the well-known account of the mould attacking the culture on his laboratory dish. The question does not, however, get an agreed answer from historians:

Source 3

Robert P. Hudson, *Disease and its Control*, 1983.

Fleming's role in the story of penicillin generally has been exaggerated. …He was hampered by his inability to purify the substance, by his lack of chemical knowledge, and by his inability to find a collaborator with the requisite chemical knowledge.…There is evidence that he was not convinced that the problem of isolating and purifying the active fraction of penicillium could be overcome.…Credit for purifying penicillin and for overcoming the many problems of mass production belongs to Howard Florey and his team of Oxford investigators, most notably Ernst Chain, who pointed the group towards penicillin in the first place.

Source 4

Roderick E. McGrew, *Encyclopedia of Medical History*, 1985.

peripheral Minor.

Though Fleming, Florey and Chain were given a joint Nobel prize, there has been a considerable argument over the public image of Fleming's role. The historical records are now clear, and the different contributions made by the leading figures are hardly in doubt. Alexander Fleming identified penicillin, preserved the mould, and called attention to its properties. Florey and the Oxford Circle developed penicillin.…Though the contributions differed, and the exaggerated reverence for Sir Alexander Fleming as the sole or primary contributor to penicillin is not justified, it is clear that he can no more be written out of the story or reduced to a peripheral role than can his Oxford colleagues.

Questions

1 a In what ways are the arguments in Sources 3 and 4 similar?

b In what ways do the arguments in Sources 3 and 4 differ?

2 Using the other Sources and information, which of Sources 3 and 4 do you find more convincing?

3 Another example of historians disagreeing is about how the *penicillium* spores got into Fleming's specimen dish. Is this debate more – or less – important than the debate on what Fleming contributed to the development of penicillin? Give reasons.

Unit 14 · The state and health

Until the twentieth century, governments avoided responsibility for the health of the people in their everyday lives. This, however, changed in two main stages – as a result of deliberate government policy based on political decisions. In the first period (1905–14) the Liberal government introduced a series of reforms. In the words of David Lloyd George, the Chancellor of the Exchequer, these were intended to cover the essential needs of people 'from the cradle to the grave'. The second period, which started during the Second World War and extended beyond 1945, saw the introduction of the welfare state, the key part of which was the National Health Service.

14.1 Liberal reforms, 1905–14

In 1905 a Liberal government was set up after twenty years of Conservative control. Their leader, first Campbell-Bannerman, then Asquith, took this as a popular vote of approval for their proposals for reform. They therefore pressed ahead with the biggest programme of social change Britain had ever experienced.

Why reform?

There were several reasons for this burst of activity. The first was the overwhelming weight of evidence that something needed to be done. The most widely publicised evidence was the Rowntree survey carried out at the turn of the century. Published in 1901 as a book called *Poverty, A Study in Town Life*, this described the life of the poorer section of the working class:

Source 1

B. Seebohm Rowntree, *Poverty, A Study in Town Life*, 1901.

Practically the whole of this class are living either in a state of actual poverty, or so near to that state that they are liable to sink into it at any moment. They live constantly from hand to mouth. So long as the wage earner is in work the family manages to get along, but a week's illness or lack of work means short rations or running into debt, or more often both of these.

The second reason was the shock produced by the Boer War of 1899–1902. This showed that a large part of the working class were unfit for military duty. Of about 680,000 volunteers, 35 per cent were declared unfit and turned down. This caused a major outcry in the press and the government was so worried that it appointed an Inquiry into Physical Deterioration.

Third, there was a strong political influence for social change. In British history there has usually been one party pressing harder than the other for reform. At this time the Liberals were much more in favour of change than the Conservatives. Parties can also change their views internally as well. Between 1868 and 1894 the Liberal Party had been led by W. E. Gladstone who, in his time, had had the reputation of being a reformer. But he had stopped short of the idea of the welfare state. Somehow, he could never accept what other members of his party were suggesting:

Source 2

W. E. Gladstone in a letter of February 1885.

The Liberalism of today…is…far from being good. Its pet idea is what they call construction – that is to say, taking into the hands of the state the business of the individual man.

This is generally seen as the view of 'Gladstonian Liberalism'. In contrast to this was the 'New Liberalism' of the early twentieth century, advanced by politicians like Lloyd George and Winston Churchill:

Source 3

A speech by Winston Churchill, reported in *The Times*, 12 October 1906.

The Government will not hesitate to use its powers to establish universal standards of life and labour, and to raise these standards as increasing productive energy permits. Liberalism must not cut itself off from…this wide and varied field of activity. We must not let ourselves be scared away from a plan just because some old woman tells us that it is socialism.

There is, perhaps, a more cynical reason why the Liberal Party should have wanted to introduce extensive reforms. The newly formed Labour Party was challenging the Liberals for the working-class vote. It made sound political sense for the Liberals to divert support from Labour and win this back. The best way of doing this was to introduce reforms which would mainly affect the working class.

The reforms

The Liberal governments of 1905–14 introduced a large number of changes. These are covered extensively in the Longman History Project, *People in Change*, pages 98–101. We shall therefore deal with those which have a special connection with health.

Source 4

The medical inspection of a child at school in 1912.

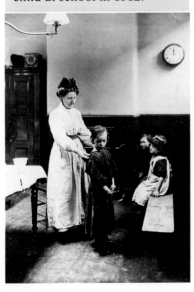

Each part of the population was affected by Liberal legislation. Children benefited from several changes. Local Education Authorities were given the power to provide free school meals for children of the poor in 1906. In 1907 a School Medical Service was set up, along with compulsory medical inspections. School clinics followed in 1912 for children recommended for treatment.

The elderly face a major problem – failing health. At the beginning of the century this was made worse by their having to work well into old age. A major change occurred when, in 1908, Lloyd George introduced Old Age Pensions. People over seventy, earning less than £26 a year, now received a pension of 25p per week for a single person and $37\frac{1}{2}$p per week for a married couple. This made retirement a practical possibility.

Workers also benefited. One of the main problems they had faced was how they would live when they were prevented from working. The National Insurance Act of 1911 covered the two reasons most likely for this. Part 1 was concerned mainly with health, part 2 with unemployment.

Source 5

'The dawn of hope', a poster advertising National Insurance, 1911.

In both cases the idea was that the worker contributed to a fund from his weekly wage. Further amounts were added by the employer and state. The total would gradually increase through investment and be used only if needed. This is the basic idea of 'insurance'. The worker would receive 37½p per week if prevented by illness from working for up to fifteen weeks.

How important were the Liberal reforms?

There was much that was positive. This was the first time in Britain that any government had taken upon itself a policy to uplift the lower levels of the population. The Liberals presented what they were doing as a new dawn (Source 5) and as a movement in the right direction (Source 6). Lloyd George, who found the funding for these changes, was seen in various roles by the media. *Punch* was usually favourable.

Source 6

'The right ticket for you!', a leaflet explaining National Insurance, 1911.

Sources 7 and 8

Two *Punch* cartoons on the Lloyd George budget of 1908.

RICH FARE.

The Giant Lloyd-Gorgibuster: "FEE, FI, FO, FAT,
I SMELL THE BLOOD OF A PLUTOCRAT;
BE HE ALIVE OR BE HE DEAD,
I'LL GRIND HIS BONES TO MAKE MY BREAD."

THE PHILANTHROPIC HIGHWAYMAN.

Mr. Lloyd-George. "I'LL MAKE 'EM PITY THE AGED POOR!"

There was also much spontaneous gratitude. Some of this was recorded in the recollections of Flora Thompson, a Post Office clerk at the time:

Source 9

Flora Thompson, *Lark Rise to Candleford*, 1945.

When the Old Age Pensions began, life was transformed for such aged cottagers. They were relieved of anxiety. They were suddenly rich. Independent for life! At first when they went to the Post Office to draw it, tears of gratitude would run down the cheeks of some, and they would say as they picked up their money, 'God bless that Lord George!'

It is, of course, possible to criticise the reforms. The amounts provided were very small, even by the standard of the day. Nothing was done about housing, which had been one of the main causes of poor health throughout the nineteenth century. The health provisions of the 1911 Insurance Act were also very selective and did not cover workers' wives and children. The changes were open to the charge that they did not go far enough. Part of the Labour Party blamed this on the whole idea of insurance:

Source 10

A statement from six members of the Labour Party opposing the National Insurance Bill (from *The Times*, 7 December 1911).

We have opposed the Bill, first because of its contributory character. By exacting contributions from the workers to finance the so-called schemes of social reform, we are not only adopting a policy which can bring no real improvement, but we are continuing a practice which two generations of experience have proved to be ineffective and impractical.

Questions

1   In what ways are Sources 5 and 6 propaganda? How effective are they?

2   Explain the meaning of Sources 7 and 8. What do they show of the sympathies of the cartoonist?

3   On what grounds did part of the Labour Party oppose the 1911 Insurance Act (Source 10)? Why do you think the rest of the Labour Party supported the Liberal reforms?

14.2 The formation of the welfare state and the National Health Service

Between the wars the system set up by the Liberals was changed in some ways. For example, efforts were made by various governments to improve housing. They also brought down the pensionable age to sixty-five and added provision for widows (at 50p per week) and orphans (at $37\frac{1}{2}$p per week).

There were, however, no major changes. This was largely because the British economy experienced great difficulties between the wars and the government's main concern was always unemployment. There was very little chance at this stage to extend the range of welfare services. Then, during and immediately after the Second World War, there was another burst of reforms.

How did the welfare state originate?

The Second World War

The Second World War did more than the First to stimulate the government into introducing health measures for the benefit of the British people. In 1940, for example, Local Educational Authorities were ordered to provide free school meals. This was a result of the shortages caused by war which affected everyone:

Source 1

An extract from an official report, 1941.

There is no question of capacity to pay; we may find the children of well-to-do parents and the children of the poor suffering alike from an inability to get the food they need.

The same applied to milk. In 1943 Winston Churchill made a broadcast to the nation:

Source 2

An extract from Churchill's radio broadcast of 1943.

There is no finer investment for any community than putting milk into babies.

Source 3

Cartoon from the *Daily Mirror* showing the Hand of War providing food and vitamins to a child.

Vitamins too were more generally available. The *Daily Mirror* was in no doubt about the reason for all this sudden activity (see Source 3).

The Second World War also brought more awareness of what poverty was like. Between 1939 and 1940 many children were evacuated from the inner cities to avoid German bombing. The people with whom they stayed were often shocked to see what these children brought with them. The writer H. G. Wells pointed out the importance of this:

Source 4

Extract from *The New World Order*, by H. G. Wells (1940).

Parasites and skin diseases, vicious habits and insanitary practices have been spread, as if in a passion of equalitarian propaganda, from the slums of such centres as Glasgow, London and Liverpool, throughout the length and breadth of the land.

The Beveridge Report

In 1942, in the middle of the Second World War, a senior civil servant called William Beveridge brought out a report examining the existing welfare services. He identified five great problems, which he called 'giants'. These were Want, Disease, Ignorance, Squalor and Idleness. He aimed to replace the existing system of Social Insurance, which dealt with Want, by Social Security, which would deal with all five.

The plan was not immediately put into practice. Instead, the government introduced several White Papers which outlined changes which it intended to introduce after the war. But these did not necessarily mean the full welfare state proposed by Beveridge.

Then, on 5 July 1945, the Labour Party, under Clement Attlee, heavily defeated the Conservatives under Winston Churchill. Attlee formed a new Labour government and announced that he would introduce the welfare state. The National Health Service, which was part of this, was introduced by Act of Parliament in 1946.

Source 5

Extracts from the National Health Service Act, 1946.

1 (1) It shall be the duty of the Minister of Health...to promote the establishment in England and Wales of a comprehensive health service designed to secure improvement in the physical and mental health of the people of England and Wales and for the prevention, diagnosis and treatment of illness....

(2) The services so provided shall be free of charge, except where any provision of this Act expressly provides for the making and recovery of charges.

The introduction of the National Health Service in 1948 meant that everyone was entitled to free treatment. Doctors were given a salary by the state. Hospitals were nationalised, or taken over by the state, and local authorities were responsible for providing free medical services. Other laws for the welfare state were the National Insurance Act (1946) and the National Assistance Act (1946).

Was the welfare state a revolutionary change?

It is often asked whether the introduction of the NHS was a complete break with the past. Was it a revolution – that is, a sudden and huge change? Or was there continuity with the earlier part of the twentieth century?

Some historians argue that it was a complete transformation and that what really made the difference was the experience of the Second World War:

Source 6

Maurice Bruce, *The Coming of the Welfare State*, 1961.

The decisive event in the evolution of the Welfare State was the Second World War, which, coming as it did after a long period of distress...challenged the British people to round off the system of social security....The war speeded changes and left a country markedly different and markedly more humane and civilised than that of 1939.

Others believe that there is continuity with the Liberal period. The Liberal governments had, after all, laid the foundations for state involvement. The method they chose was 'insurance', which was precisely the means used in the welfare state after 1945. People continued to contribute, through National Insurance contributions, to protection against sickness and unemployment. The difference was that the benefits provided by the state were much greater.

Questions

1 a Why did William Beveridge refer to the five social problems as 'giants'?
   b How effective is this description?

2 How do the duties and services referred to in Source 5 differ from the health reforms made by the Liberals before 1914?

3 Examine Sources 2 to 6. To what extent do Sources 2 to 5 reinforce what is said in Source 6?

14.3 Opposition to the formation of the welfare state and the NHS

The welfare state and, in particular, the NHS met opposition from two quarters. One was from the leader of the Conservative Party. While he had been Prime Minister during the Second World War, Churchill had already had reservations about the ideas within the Beveridge Report. Many other Conservatives agreed with his view that the National Health Service would be too much for the country's economy to bear:

Source 1

From Winston Churchill's Cabinet notes, 14 February 1943.

A dangerous optimism is growing up about the conditions it will be possible to establish here after the war....The question steals across the mind whether we are not committing our forty-five million people to tasks beyond their compass, and laying on them burdens beyond their capacity to bear.

Churchill also argued that the welfare state as a whole could only be introduced by a policy of socialism. While he was fighting the 1945 election he made some rather gloomy predictions about what would happen if there were a Labour government:

Source 2

From an election broadcast for the Conservative Party made by Winston Churchill in June 1945.

...no socialist system can be established without a political police. They [a Labour government] would have to fall back on some form of Gestapo.

Sources 3 and 4

Two cartoons showing the expected effects of the welfare state.

WIFE, CHILD AND WELFARE STATE TO SUPPORT

Opposition also came from the British Medical Association, as the following survey shows:

Source 5

The views of members of the British Medical Association in 1948 on the National Health Service Act.

In favour of the NHS Act	4,734
Opposed to the NHS Act	40,814

Some members of the BMA had already expressed their opposition to the idea of a National Health Service back in 1943:

Source 6

From the *British Medical Journal*, 1943.

If this happens, then doctors will no longer be an independent, learned and liberal profession, but will instead form a service of technicians controlled by bureaucrats and by local men and women entirely ignorant of medical matters.

Many doctors defied the attempts made by Aneurin Bevan, the Labour Minister of Health to introduce a national health service, and refused to co-operate with the new Health Service. The welfare state was therefore seriously threatened. Eventually a compromise was reached – that doctors could have private patients as well as receiving a salary from the NHS.

Questions

1 Explain the meaning of Sources 3 and 4. What do the cartoonists think of the welfare state?

2 Look at Sources 1 and 2 in 14.3. Then refer to Source 3 in 14.1 and Source 2 in 14.2. Do these sources, taken together, show that Winston Churchill changed his mind about social reforms?

14.4 The operation of the National Health Service since 1945

The welfare state was intended to fulfil Lloyd George's aim to provide care 'from cradle to grave'. This included the best possible facilities to ensure safe births; care by doctors and hospitals whenever needed; financial help like supplementary benefit and child benefit; and pensions at the age of sixty-five for men and sixty for women. The key part of the welfare state is the NHS. But since its formation in 1948 it has come under more and more pressure. There are several reasons for this. For one thing, the population profile is changing, with the average age creeping up. This means that the NHS has a larger proportion of elderly patients who need more regular support. Also, technological progress means that there is always more expensive equipment to buy. This has been made more difficult by periods of economic stagnation and by ever-growing competition for funding to deal with other problems like unemployment. Increasingly in the 1990s, questions have been asked about the future of the NHS.

Is the future of the National Health Service safe?

Whether the NHS is safe depends on what we consider should be done about its funding. Everyone agrees that it has financial problems – but not about the solutions to these.

One possibility, explored by millions of people in Britain, is to take out private health insurance. There are arguments for and against this approach. On the positive side, private health insurance helps reduce waiting lists within the NHS by removing some of the patients it would otherwise have to treat. It also means that more people can be treated quickly, which benefits the economy since they can then return to work. On the other hand, there is much criticism of queue-jumping by private patients. It has also been argued that private medicine takes

Source 1

Promotional material from a company which offers private health insurance.

investment and resources away from the NHS. To some it is seen as the thin end of a wedge which will remove the NHS except as a safety net for the poor who cannot afford to pay any form of private insurance.

Few people want to do away with private medical insurance. But there is a considerable difference of opinion about what sort of role private medicine should play. Some politicians would encourage it as much as possible:

Source 2

From a speech made by the Prime Minister, Margaret Thatcher, in October 1982.

> Of course, we welcome the growth of private health insurance. There is no contradiction between that and supporting the National Health Service. It brings in more money, helps to reduce waiting lists and stimulates new treatments and techniques.

This view was given a hostile reception by the Labour Party in 1985:

Source 3

From 'Breaking the nation', a document produced by the Labour Party Research Department in 1985.

> The Tories are undermining the NHS from all sides. They are proceeding step by step towards a two-tier health service – a growing commercial sector for the wealthy and healthy, and a deprived, demoralized public service for the rest.

Source 4

Headline from the *Independent* 13 August 1994.

No 2,439

Cradle to grave NHS buried by Government

Two recent trends within the NHS have also caused political controversy. The first was the decision by the government in August 1994 that NHS hospitals should no longer keep elderly patients who are not being treated for a medical condition. Instead, they should be transferred to nursing homes. The fees would be paid from the patient's savings. This would then release beds for those people who had an illness which could be treated. But there were accusations from the press that the 'cradle to grave' idea of the NHS was being worn away (see Source 4).

Another controversial idea was that various NHS hospitals might be privatised – or run by commercial companies. The intention was to make them more efficient and cost-effective. This would mean a better service to their patients. But the Labour Party did not agree:

Source 5

The view of David Blunkett, Labour's spokesman on health, August 1994.

> This is yet more evidence that the government is deadly serious about allowing the private sector to profit by providing NHS services...the NHS is being sold off bit by bit.

Questions

1 Write a discussion between two people looking at the advertisement shown in Source 1.

2 Mrs Thatcher said, while she was Prime Minister, that 'the NHS is safe in our hands' (i.e. under a Conservative government). Do you agree?

Unit 15 · Women and medicine

15.1   What women have contributed to medicine

In Units 11 and 12 we saw the struggle by women such as Florence Nightingale and Elizabeth Garrett to achieve equality with men. Clearly they had only partly succeeded. One historian argues that the control of medicine by men continued through the twentieth century as well:

Source 1

Jeanne Achterberg, *Woman as Healer*, 1991.

Historically, whenever women have been welcomed back into the healing fold, it has been to supply the 'caring' to the 'curing', the latter always having been associated with men and power.

Women in the First World War: caring or curing?

The biggest impact on women in medicine in the early twentieth century came from the First World War. This greatly increased the demand for nurses and therefore continued what the Crimean War had started. Many more women enrolled as nurses and there was less opposition to women doing war-work here than in any other area. This was because Florence Nightingale had already established nursing as a 'woman's profession'. Elsewhere, as in munitions and transport, there was some opposition to work being done by women. It could be said, therefore, that nursing led the way for women's emancipation.

Source 2

A photograph showing nurses working with the sick and wounded on the Western Front.

The contribution of women to the care of the wounded was considerable. Voluntary Aid Detachments (VADs) and the First Aid Nursing Yeomanry (FANYs) left for France shortly after the outbreak of war. There were also nurses from hospitals and from the British Red Cross. Their experiences were often terrible, and women were brought more directly into contact with the horrors of war than ever before.

Source 3

A British propaganda poster:
Red Cross or Iron Cross?

Everyone recognised the value of the nurses' work – and the government even used it as propaganda against the enemy (see Source 3).

The war also saw a considerable increase in the number of women acting as doctors and surgeons. This was due largely to the example set by Elsie Inglis, Flora Murray and Louisa Garrett Anderson, who worked in a surgery in Endell Street with wounded soldiers evacuated from France:

Source 4   Flora Murray, *Women as Army Surgeons*, 1920.

The surgeons spent all their mornings in the wards, and most of their afternoons in the operating theatre, where it was not unusual to have a list of twenty or thirty cases on each operating day.

Growing equality?

The First World War greatly improved the position of women generally. For example, they received the vote in 1918. Can it be said that women continued to make progress towards equality in medicine after 1918? The answer is complex and needs to be broken down into sections.

A VICTORY OVER TYPHUS: CHLOROMYCETIN SYNTHESISED FOR THE FIRST TIME, BY DR. MILDRED C. REBST

1 Equality as specialists?

On the one hand, there were many signs of growing equality in the more specialised areas of medicine. The number of women doctors continued to rise after the First World War and was further increased by the introduction of the National Health Service (see Unit 14). In addition, more women entered the medical schools.

There were also major individual achievements. Dr Mildred Berstock, for example, developed an inoculation against typhus. All this was assisted by laws which were introduced to prevent discrimination against women.

Source 5

The proportion of women entering medical schools in Britain.

by mid-1960s: 25%
by mid-1970s: 35%
by mid-1980s: 46%

Source 6

The cover of the *Illustrated London News* showing the achievement of Dr Mildred Berstock in synthesising an inoculation against typhus.

Source 7

From the Sex Disqualification (Removal) Act, 1919.

A person shall not be disqualified by sex or marriage from the exercise of any public functions, or from being appointed to or holding any civil or judicial office or post, from entering or assuming or carrying on any civil profession or vocation.

Source 8

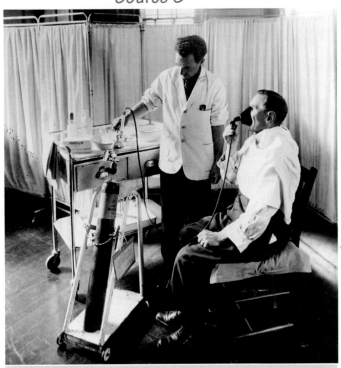

Assistant male nurse at St John's Hospital, London, 1947.

These were eventually followed by two other laws. The Equal Pay Act, 1970, stated that women should receive the same salary as a man for the same job (previously there had been different rates for men and women). The Sex Discrimination Act, 1975, made it illegal to discriminate between men and women in making appointments or promotions. Both of these are enforced by the Equal Opportunities Commission.

There have also been changes in nursing with the introduction of men into the profession. For the first time since the days of Florence Nightingale nursing is no longer seen entirely as women's work (see Source 8).

On the other hand, there are several ways in which real equality has still not been achieved. Nursing, for example, still consists mainly of women, which is the main reason for its relatively low pay when compared with most other professions. There is also an uneven distribution of jobs at the top end of the medical profession:

Source 9

Jeanne Achterberg, *Woman as Healer*, 1991.

While mainstream medicine remains male-dominated, the ranks of nurses continue to be almost entirely female. Nurses function under two layers of authority: hospital and physician....It is worth noting that women in training currently enjoy a greater success rate than men, though the current structure of Higher Training makes it particularly difficult for women junior doctors to progress to senior positions.

2 Equality as non-specialists?

The vast majority of women are neither doctors nor nurses. Yet they continue to have the main role of health care within the family. This applies as much in Britain as it does in other parts of the world:

Source 10

Women as Providers of Health Care, World Health Organisation, Geneva, 1987.

[The responsibilities of women as providers of non-formal health care normally include:] (a) taking decisions concerning the health care of family members; (b) rearing children on healthy lines; (c) producing, selecting, preparing, and distributing the family's food; and (d) providing health services at home for convalescent, chronically ill, and disabled members of the family. Other responsibilities of women include keeping family health histories, identifying illnesses (both their own and those of others); escorting the sick for necessary care; and providing nursing care, physical therapy, and first aid.

Is this role shared between men and women? According to the same report:

Source 11

Women as Providers of Health Care, World Health Organisation, Geneva, 1987.

It is...clear that the bulk of informal health care in the home is provided by women.

Questions

1 Examine Sources 1 to 4.
a Explain Source 1.
b Is the argument in Source 1 backed by Sources 2, 5 and 6?

2 Explain the meaning of Source 3. Compare it with Source 2. In what ways is Source 3 'propaganda'?

3 'Women have achieved equality with men in medicine since 1900.' Do Sources 5 to 10 prove this?

4 Examine Source 10. Are the non-specialist medical roles carried out by women today the same as those dealt with in Unit 5?

15.2 What women have received from medicine

Women have benefited from medical changes in two ways. One is in a medical sense, especially in childbirth. The other is in a social sense, through contraception.

Developments in obstetrics

Giving birth has become steadily safer since 1900. It often takes place in a maternal unit in a hospital, with the assistance of doctors and midwives. Specialist equipment is available to monitor the progress made by the foetus before birth, and a range of anaesthetics is available to reduce the pain experienced by women giving birth.

Source 1

Expectant mother in hospital.

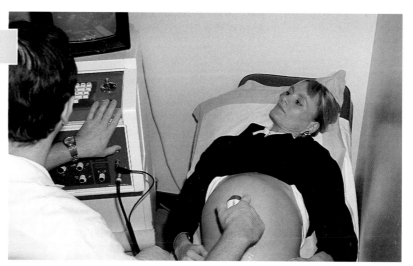

The result of this care is the reduction in the death rate of women.

Source 2

Philip Rhodes, *An Outline History of Medicine*, 1985.

Maternal deaths
1928: 4.42 per 1,000 births
1975: 0.11 per 1,000 births

There has also been progress in assisting women to conceive. Fertility is sometimes increased by surgery and sometimes by external fertilisation of the ova – the so-called test-tube baby technique developed by Patrick Steptoe and R. G. Edwards in the 1970s.

Developments in birth control

Contraception gives women more sexual freedom by controlling the chances of pregnancy. Two contributions to this have been particularly important.

One was the work of Dr Marie Stopes. Born in Scotland in 1880, she graduated from London University and took a Doctorate of Botany in Germany and a Doctorate of Science in London. She wrote a book called *Married Love*, which was published in Britain in 1918. It gave open and detailed advice about marriage, sex and family planning. In 1921 she opened the country's first birth control clinic. In 1930 she formed the National Birth Control Council which in 1939 became the Family Planning Association, with more than 60 birth-control clinics around the country. Marie Stopes is most associated with making contraception acceptable socially:

Source 3

The view of Margaret Pike, chairman of the Family Planning Association.

In a final estimate, Marie Stopes may well prove to have been one of the most important and outstanding influences of the twentieth century – a judgement with which, one feels sure, she would be in complete agreement.

At the time, however, she was able to advise only on condoms and diaphragms. The main breakthrough with contraception was the Pill, which originated with the research of Gregory Goodwin Pincus in the 1950s. This proved more reliable than other forms of contraception and also gave women more choice than they had had before over whether or not they became pregnant.

Question

Look at Source 3.
a How does it emphasise the social importance of medical change?
b How far is it likely to have been influenced by the occupation of its author?

Unit 16 · Alternative medicine

The changes we have been examining have taken place largely in the mainstream, or at the centre of medicine. There have also been important developments at the fringe, or edge, of medicine. These come under the heading of alternative medicine.

16.1 The meaning of alternative medicine

We must be careful to separate **alternative medicine** from another term often used – **supplementary medicine**. The latter consists of practitioners like physiotherapists and occupational therapists who work closely with doctors and nurses to restore the body or mind to working order. There are also prosthetists and orthotists who specialise in fitting artificial body parts. At all times these practitioners supplement, or add to, mainstream medicine. Alternative medicine, on the other hand, offers the patient a different type of treatment and often competes with mainstream medicine.

What are the branches of alternative medicine?

The idea of alternative medicine is very old and connects up with the methods we saw in Unit 7. Since 1900, however, six branches have become particularly well known.

Source 1

A drawing showing an adjustment by a chiropractor.

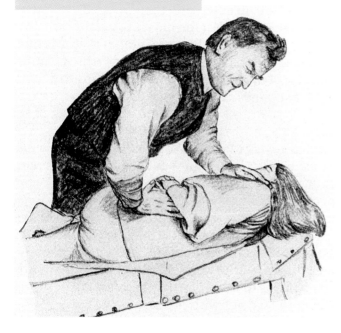

Chiropractic

This deals with joint disorders, and disorders in the back. Chiropractors work by manipulation rather than by operation. That is to say, they use their hands and not scalpels; this is what separates them from surgeons.

Manipulation had been widely used in the Ancient World, especially by Hippocrates and Galen. There was then a long gap in this type of treatment until the success of Sarah Mapp in the eighteenth century. The next development occurred in the United States, where D. D. Palmer claimed in the nineteenth century to have rediscovered the technique of manipulation. He said that this could help many problems and ailments, which were often caused by nerves being trapped by vertebrae which were out of position.

Chiropractic spread to Europe shortly before the outbreak of the First World War and to Britain in 1925. The British Chiropractic Association was set up, and in 1965 a college was opened in Bournemouth to train chiropractors. Since 1988 it has been possible to take a degree course there.

Osteopathy

Osteopathy grew out of the same roots as chiropractic but has a more general idea of health:

Source 2

Leon Chaitow, *Osteopathy, a Complete Health-care System*, 1982.

Osteopathy is a system of health care which recognizes that the self-healing, self-regulating ability of the body is dependent on a number of factors, including favourable environmental conditions,...adequate nutrition....It places special emphases upon the importance of body mechanics, and uses manipulative techniques to detect and correct faulty structure and function.

The founder of osteopathy was Andrew Taylor Still, an American. In Britain three colleges offer full-time courses in osteopathy.

Homoeopathy

The founder of homoeopathy was Samuel Hahnemann, in 1755. He believed that the healing process should be promoted naturally. He strongly opposed purging the body using strong drugs. This is still the approach today; treatment is based on a 'symptom picture' of the patient. Many drugs are thus considered unnecessary.

Source 3

Andrew Lockie, *The Family Guide to Homeopathy*, 1990.

A homeopathic remedy is one which produces the same symptoms as those the sick person complains of, and in doing so sharply provokes the body into throwing them off. 'Like may be cured by like'...is the basic principle.

Acupuncture

This started in ancient China. The Emperor Huan Ti and his physician, Chi Po, worked out the theory behind acupuncture some 4,600 years ago. It came to Europe as late as the seventeenth century AD, and became established in Britain only from the 1960s.

Acupuncture involves the use of needles inserted into carefully chosen parts of the body. The needles are then rotated, or more recently, used in electro-magnetic fields. One idea is to create harmony within the body between all the opposing forces. Another theory is that various points on the body are linked to internal organs which can be affected by the use of needles at these points. Acupuncture is often used for headaches, especially migraines, and nervous disorders.

Psychotherapy

This is a general term which covers two types of practitioner. One is the psychiatrist who has a medical training and is fully recognised as part of the medical establishment. The other is the lay psychotherapist, who practises without a medical qualification.

Both provide treatment based on a process known as psychoanalysis, and is intended to treat problems of the mind rather than of the body. The method is based on the ideas of Sigmund Freud, who worked in Vienna in the late nineteenth and early twentieth centuries. Patients are encouraged to relax and to bring to the surface things they are trying to forget or repress, for them to be dealt with properly.

Hypnotherapy

Sometimes hypnosis is used. This might have two purposes. One is to make the patient reveal hidden problems. Or it can make the patient act in a certain way. The first method overlaps into psychotherapy and is widely used. The second is more controversial and cannot be used to make the patient do anything which is morally unacceptable.

Spiritual healing

In some ways this is the most controversial of all forms of alternative medicine. It has a history going back thousands of years, but has made something of a comeback from the mid-twentieth century, especially in the United States.

Spiritual healers aim to do several things. They try to bring about direct contact with the god-force in which the patient believes. They aim to restore the internal harmony and balance which the illness has upset. And they try to get rid of the patient's anxiety and fear. Spiritual healing is done either through contact healing, or the laying on of hands, or distant healing through the meditation of the healer.

Herbal medicine

This has an ancient background and, unlike chiropractic or acupuncture, has no particular founder. Its popularity can be seen by the remedies which are available, for a variety of ailments, in health food shops and chemists today.

Questions

1 Explain the similarities and differences between chiropractic and osteopathy.

2 Some of the forms of alternative medicine today are older than those practised in the eighteenth century.
a Give examples of these, and
b Explain whether you think this makes them less reliable. Give reasons. (You should also use material from Unit 7.)

16.2 Attitudes to alternative medicine

There are two main reasons why people have been attracted to alternative medicine. First, some patients are attracted by the possibility of a cure for their condition without surgery. They may also be suspicious of strong drugs. This is often put across in books about alternative medicine. Second, people have become more aware of healthy lifestyles.

Alternative medicine is as much concerned about maintaining health as it is about curing illness. Awareness of mental and physical health has increased as a result of massive publicity in magazines and on television. Most doctors are heavily worked and do not have the time to reassure patients. These reasons for the flourishing of alternative medicine are now widely accepted.

Is there a close link between alternative and established medicines?

As we have seen, doctors co-operate closely with the professions supplementary to medicine. This applies especially to physiotherapy. A department of physiotherapy is to be found in almost every large hospital and doctors often prescribe treatment by physiotherapy following, or instead of, a surgical operation. Are there similar links with alternative medicine?

Links

Some doctors refer their patients to an alternative medical practitioner in cases where drugs have not had a permanent effect or where there is no need for surgery. Doctors often do this when they consider the problem not to be serious.

For their part, most practitioners of alternative medicine are anxious not to give the impression that they are competing with doctors.

At one time it was a criminal offence for a doctor to recommend treatment by an osteopath. This is no longer the case and referrals are often made.

Much the same applies to acupuncture. Until very recently doctors were extremely doubtful about its use. But during the past thirty years doctors have become more familiar with it. Many have trained in its use and some hospitals make provision for acupuncture.

Suspicions

On the other hand, doctors have a long history of suspicion of alternative medicine. The BMA were strongly opposed to many early practitioners and often struck off the register doctors who co-operated with them. Even today, many forms of alternative medicine, like homoeopathy, do not feature in the training of a doctor. Many doctors remain doubtful about whether alternative medicine actually works. They point out that there is rarely any scientific proof to back the claims for cures.

Such doubts mean that alternative medicine still has no official standing. There are no laws covering many of the alternative medical practices. Anyone, for example, can set up as an osteopath. Practitioners of alternative medicine want official recognition by being registered. But the application made by the British Chiropractic Association was rejected and the government refused to consider an appeal. Parliament rejected an attempt by Mrs Butler in 1976 (see Source E) to get through a bill setting up a register for osteopaths. There is therefore some way to go before the status of alternative medicine catches up with that of supplementary medicine.

Questions

Study Sources A to G and answer the questions which follow.

Source A

A photograph showing manipulation by an osteopath.

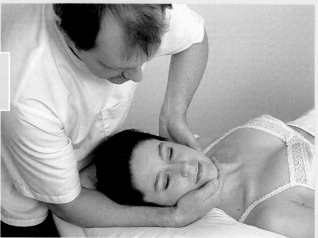

Source B

A photograph showing an acupuncturist at work on a patient.

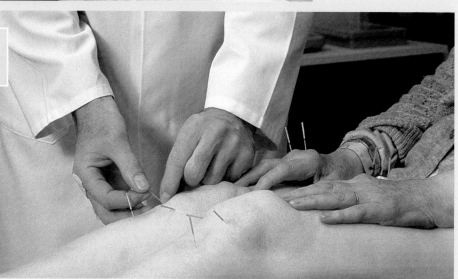

Source C

An extract from the report of a survey on the popularity of alternative therapies, in which 2,000 people took part. (Adapted from *Journal of Alternative Medicine*, July 1984, p.1)

Types of alternative therapy personally experienced	Tried by %	Satisfied? Yes %	No %
Herbal medicine	12	73	18
Osteopathy	6	73	14
Massage	6	82	9
Homeopathy	4	66	16
Acupuncture	3	50	47
Chiropractic	2	68	19
Hypnotherapy	2	43	50
Psychotherapy	2	75	12

Source D

Dr Caroline M. Shreeve, *The Alternative Dictionary of Symptoms and Cures*, 1986.

Diazepam A tranquillizer.

Certainly...it is better for many patients to use a mild herbal tranquilliser for 'nerves' than a pharmacological synthetic compound such as Diazepam or to treat an upset stomach with, say, slippery elm rather than a standard antacid.

Source E

An extract from a speech in the House of Commons given by Mrs Joyce Butler, MP, 7 April 1976.

There is a growing interest among the general public, and even within the medical profession, in various less orthodox medical procedures....The interest often comes from practical experience of the success of such treatment when more usual methods have failed. Some of it is also undoubtedly a reaction against excessive drug therapy and a search for more natural methods of treatment.

Source F

Thorsons Introductory Guide to Chiropractic, 1987.

In Great Britain, the general practitioner is firmly established as the doctor of primary contact for health care, and the co-ordinator of health services for his patient. There seems little point in chiropractors attempting to usurp [try to take over] that role. On the other hand, even if spinal manipulative therapy does become part of the general practitioner's training, they will not be able to devote sufficient time to training or to the practice of this work.

Source G

Dr Caroline M. Shreeve, *The Alternative Dictionary of Symptoms and Cures,* 1986.

I must add a cautionary word. It is vital, in the case of all acute or long-standing health problems, to obtain at least a definitive diagnosis from an orthodox doctor, and (except in rare instances) to undergo the recommended course of treatment, perhaps complemented by one or two alternative treatments....My personal choice...would be to combine the best that orthodox medicine and the appropriate alternative medicine have to offer.

Questions

1 How might an historian of the future enquiring into the growth of alternative medicine use Sources A, B and C?

2 **a** To what extent do the other Sources agree with the findings of Source C?
   b Use your own knowledge to provide other reasons for the growing popularity of modern alternative medicine.

3 **a** What evidence is there in Sources D, E, F and G for (i) rivalry and (ii) harmony between conventional and alternative medicine in the twentieth century?
   b Might the authors of Sources D, E, F and G have different motives for their views?

4 Using any of these Sources, and your own knowledge, say whether you consider alternative medicine has, in the twentieth century, become more important in relation to conventional medicine than in earlier centuries.

This Unit draws together the information in this book to provide an overall perspective under three headings.

Public health provision

In the Ancient World the state took responsibility for essentials like the provision of fresh water (**Unit 1.1**). This lapsed during the Middle Ages (**Unit 1.2**). The state avoided imposing any controls on public health throughout the period 1450–1750. Instead, it merely introduced occasional laws about the organisation and training of surgeons (**Unit 4.2**) or about hospitals (**Unit 4.3**).

During the nineteenth century the catalyst for change was fear of what might happen if no attempts were made to check deadly diseases. Hence the government introduced compulsory vaccination against smallpox (**Unit 8.1**). Regarding the cholera threat (**Unit 9.1**) there was a long debate about the government's role (**Unit 9.2**). In the second half of the nineteenth century, three levels of responsibility emerged for public health and living conditions: central government, local authorities and private enterprise (**Unit 9.3**). Meanwhile, the government was also defining who should be allowed to practise medicine (**Units 12.1, 12.2**).

However, the state had not yet accepted responsibility for the health of its people in an everyday sense. The turning point came with the reforms of the Liberals between 1905 and 1914 (**Unit 14.1**). These introduced the idea of care 'from the cradle to the grave'. The welfare state was built on these foundations, with a boost from the conditions of the Second World War (**Unit 14.2**). The most important part of the welfare state was the National Health Service. Now it is faced by some problems: in particular, should the state's role now be reduced (**Unit 14.4**)? Issues of public health in the twentieth century have become influenced by party politics (**Units 14.1, 14.2, 14.3, 14.4**).

Medical knowledge and training

Medical knowledge covers a large area. One of the most important forms was knowledge about the causes of, and cures for, various diseases. The Ancient World had established a connection between dirt and disease (**Unit 1.1**), something that was largely lost in the Middle Ages (**Unit 1.2**). Between 1450 and 1800 the behaviour of diseases remained a mystery (**Unit 6.1**), and none of the ideas for treating them considered microbes – even though the microscope had been invented and microbes discovered (**Unit 3.1**). During the nineteenth century much work was done on microbiology (**Unit 8.2**), which helped surgery through the use of antiseptics (**Unit 10.2**). In the twentieth century huge strides were made with the development of antibiotics and sulphonamides (**Unit 13.3**) and vaccines for previously lethal diseases (**Unit 13.1**).

Knowledge about anatomy and surgery remained static for over a thousand years after the collapse of the Roman empire. By 1450 the works of Galen were still most influential. The Renaissance, however, brought new influences and new ideas (**Unit 2**). A breakthrough in knowledge occurred in the seventeenth century (**Unit 3.1**), especially with Harvey's work on the circulation of blood (**Unit 3.2**). This had little immediate effect on surgery (**Unit 4.1**), in which the major developments were the discovery of anaesthetics and antiseptics (**Units 10.1, 10.2**). The twentieth century brought a wide variety of new instruments and equipment. This has made possible more complex surgery (**Unit 13.2**).

Medical qualifications and training were in confusion between 1450 and 1750 (**Unit 4.2**), although more was done for the training of doctors and midwives in hospitals (**Units 4.3, 5.1**). In the nineteenth century medical qualifications were more carefully defined (**Unit 12.1**) and women were admitted to the medical profession (**Unit 12.3**). There were also developments in the training of nurses (**Unit 11.2**) and midwives (**Unit 12.2**). More women qualified as doctors after 1900, but it is doubtful whether women have achieved equality with men (**Unit 15.1**).

The treatment of the sick

The sick have been treated in several ways: by physicians, in hospitals and by alternative medicine.

The Ancient World contributed two important things to the role of the physician. These were the method of diagnosis and the Hippocratic oath (**Unit 1.1**). These have proved influential up to the present day, although the diagnostic method has improved (**Units 3.1, 13.2**). Hospitals had difficulties during the late Middle Ages and the sixteenth century, when many infirmaries of religious foundation were closed. In the seventeenth and eighteenth centuries, however, new hospitals were set up and rapid progress was made in training doctors and midwives (**Unit 4.2**). Hospital conditions, however, were deplorable. The shortcomings of nursing were shown up during the Crimean War (**Unit 11.1**) and hospitals were transformed (**Unit 11.2**). New technology and antibiotic drugs (**Unit 13**) further increased the help that could be given to patients.

One of the most important of the changes covered in this book is access to medical treatment. Before 1900 few people could afford a physician's fees. This changed with the Liberal reforms (**Unit 14.1**) and the National Health Service (**Unit 14.2**), which guaranteed medical care for all.

All this has changed the whole meaning of alternative medicine. Before the twentieth century, this was for most people the main form of help. From 1450 they relied on women healers and people with special knowledge of herbs (**Unit 7.1**). There were also quacks – people deliberately trying to exploit others (**Unit 7.2**). In the twentieth century the position of alternative medicine changed. After 1945 everyone had access to regular medicine (**Unit 14.2**), but alternative medicine also expanded rapidly, and into many different forms (**Unit 16.1**). Some of these, like chiropractic and acupuncture, are over 2,000 years old, and yet they were entirely absent from the periods 1450–1750 and 1750–1900. The relationship between mainstream and alternative medicine has experienced a few difficulties, but they have managed to live together (**Unit 16.2**).